WIND TUNNEL TALES

Memoirs of a Wind Tunnel Engineer

by
William E. Anderson

California, USA

William E. Anderson
E-mail: derputz@aol.com
18950 Consul Ave.
Corona, CA 92881

Publisher's Cataloging-In-Publication Data

Names: Anderson, William E., 1940- author.
Title: Wind tunnel tales, Memoirs of a wind tunnel engineer/ by William E. Anderson.
Description: [Corona, California] : [William E. Anderson], [2021] | Interest age level: 008-020. | Summary: Having worked for 30 years as an engineer testing aircraft designs in wind tunnels, the author shares the challenges and fun he had working on these projects.

Identifiers: ISBN 9781736311509 (paperback) | ISBN 9781736311516 (ebook)

Subjects: LCSH: Wind tunnels--Juvenile literature. | Airplanes--Testing--Juvenile literature. | Aerospace engineering--Juvenile literature. | Anderson, William E., 1940---Juvenile literature. | CYAC: Wind tunnels. | Airplanes--Testing. | Aerospace engineering. | Anderson, William E., 1940-

Classification: LCC TL547 .A54 2021 (print) | LCC TL547 (ebook) | DDC 629.13--dc23

Printed in the USA

ACKNOWLEDGMENTS

Larry Kaniut for his helpful review of the early manuscript and encouragement.

Sharon Aubrey for her generous assistance in preparing the manuscript for publishing and printing.

FORWARD

I have written this book to inspire young people to pursue a career in STEM: Science, Technology, Engineering and Technology. I fear many people think these careers are dull, boring desk jobs.

Not me! I had a ball. Sometimes, I would not see my desk for a couple of weeks at a time. I had technical challenges and worked with great people. We had lots of fun and laughter. And we did excellent work, advancing the state of the art and scientific knowledge.

My desire is for many people to have as wonderful, exciting and meaningful career as I have enjoyed.

Contents

"This job is so much fun
that we would almost do it for nothing
but don't tell anybody
because we still want the money."

R.W. Lucas

CHAPTER 1

Bob

Figure 1: Northrop 7x10 Low Speed Wind Tunnel—my "home" for 25 years.

Bob Lucas was my boss and mentor for twenty years. He worked at Northrop for forty-four years. He was a tough straight-shooter, always fair, and usually right. One of the managers of human resources once called Bob, "The best first level manager in Northrop." He was like a second father to me.

Bob tried to intimidate me on my first project at Northrop. In the fifteen feet from the door of the wind tunnel to my office door, located at the bottom of the stairs, Bob fired ten questions about my project at me.

"Yes, Bob."

"No, I haven't done that yet."

"Yes, I'll do that next."

"I don't know."

I felt Bob tested me by trying to beat me down, and I earned his respect by standing up to him and answering honestly. Later in my career, I would meet others who would try to intimidate me but respected someone who stood firm.

When I first started at Northrop, I considered myself good working with things but wasn't a "people person." Bob had faith in me and made me a lead engineer. Now my job was, as Roy Eversz put it, "Not to do it, but to get it done."

Bob taught me everything I know about leadership, and he let me learn from my many mistakes. I think Bob envied me because I had a college degree. Bob had learned instrumentation as a technician in the Air Force, but he knew more about things than anyone I'd ever known.

Figure 2: Roy and Bob

Roy Eversz was my best friend. He had worked in construction with his dad before coming to Northrop, where he learned to make estimates for a project. Roy would look over all the drawings for a large simulator project and estimate the costs and man-hours required. Our instrumentation group built and wired all the electronic equipment for the simulators.

Roy used an estimate of six minutes for each connection that had to be made in the system. He would spend hours poring over the stack of drawings, counting the number of connections that would be made. Then, he added up all his work and gave it to Bob, who looked over the project and picked out his guess about how long it would take and what it would cost.

Their two estimates were always within 10% of each other, but when the project was finished, the result was usually closer to Bob's estimate than Roy's.

Leadership books today say a lot about empowerment. Bob had an interesting way of empowering me. When a microphone for an ultrasonic leak detector broke, I told Bob I thought I could get it working again by modifying another instrument, but I wasn't sure I could restore it to original if it didn't work.

Bob's answer: "Go ahead. You haven't broken anything this week, yet."

I never had to ask permission to use my initiative again.

Later, when I returned from a meeting where I committed our department to developing "Superdrag," which was a way of improving our electronic measurement of drag requiring considerable time and resources, Bob simply said, "You put your foot into your mouth, you get it out." I had confidence to make decisions because Bob never pull the rug out from under me.

One time when we were very short of work and looking at possibly needing to lay off some people, Bob sent me around to arrange to loan some of our people to other departments, such as Flight Test, Manufacturing Technology, and Engineering Test Labs, to inquire if they might need help with electronic equipment. Usually when certain departments at Northrop were slow, others were very busy.

I knocked on many doors and found placements for three or four guys. Everyone who was loaned out was one person who would not be laid off. Later, Bob called me into his office and told me he had found a place to loan me out. He sent me to the Northrop facility at Palos Verdes, where I had first applied for a job. I was to help another man named Bob on a paper study on sensors to detect impending failures in helicopter engines. This Bob was a pilot and quite an interesting fellow, and we hit it off well. I was at Palos Verdes for several months.

Years later when I was the acting manager, we experienced another down period. I always seemed to take over when things went downhill. Just once I would have liked to have run things when we had lots of work to do. I took a page from Bob's book and went from door-to-door to find places for our people before laying anyone off.

One fellow found a home in Manufacturing Technology. A couple more were loaned to the Test Labs. Only one other manager in our labs, Dutch, a Model Shop manager, went looking for work for his people. He found some work on the TSSAM project, and they needed people who could build wiring looms for test missiles. Since it involved flight hardware, the people doing the wiring would have to be certified for the work.

Since Joe Earp had worked on the fabrication of simulator electronics, a similar kind of work, I put Joe in charge and sent him and several other techs to certification school for recertification. We set up an area in the Inlet and Duct (I & D) control room to lay out the drawings and large plywood sheets where rows of nails would facilitate the wire looms we were fabricating. Joe did a great job, and we did not have to lay anyone off.

Bob and I were both very passionate about how we did our jobs. We had many heated arguments. Bob would call Roy Eversz and me into his office to discuss how we would handle the work in the department. I argued with Bob about how we should do something. Finally, Roy gave me some of the best advice of my life, "Anderson, argue with the boss until he says, 'no' three times, then shut up!"

At one point, Bob and I argued ourselves into a corner. I was where the next thing I was going to say was, "Do it my way or I quit!" And the next thing that would come out of Bob's mouth was going to be, "Do what I say, or you're fired!" So, we both just looked at each other and neither of us said another word.

In the end, I did it his way since he was the boss.

Bob and I could argue like this, but it was always over the best way to do the work. We never took it in a personal way. Ours were professional disagreements.

Often after an argument, I would go to my office and the phone would ring. It would be Bob.

"I'm sorry, Bill. You were right," he'd say.

"No, Bob. I was wrong. You were right." I'd reply.

"No, Bill. You were right."

And we'd start to argue again. It must be one of my bad personality traits.

We had a long disagreement over the -89 stores balance. Stores balances were Northrop-made, 5-component balances used to measure the forces on bombs and missiles carried under the wings on an airplane. The -89 was a small balance tapered at both ends. (We had several identical -89 balances.) One end would fit into a mounting bracket and was indexed with roll pins. The other end fit into the store.

I was calibrating some 50-gallon fuel tanks, which were mounted on -89 balances. After each roll calibration, I would find the tail fins shifted 2 or 3 degrees from where they were before I applied the weights.

Something was slipping.

I thought that we were applying more roll loads than the balance was designed for. Our model designers assured me that the loads were right. I would call the designers over to see my problem, and they would say that everything was all right.

When I complained to Bob there was something amiss and the designers were wrong, he would get mad and insist the designers were right. "You do your job and let Design do theirs."

Precision taper joints, as we used them, were designed to fit so snugly that they would not slip, even under full loads. Further, the two parts of the taper joint were held firmly together with a screw through the middle. Finally, the roll pins were a snug fit too that should prevent any roll slippage. Still, something was slipping in roll every time I tried to calibrate the assembly. We did not resolve the problem.

Shortly later, we were preparing for a TSSAM model test at Arnold Engineering Development Complex (AEDC). The small vertical fin forces were to be measured using a Task 0.5-inch balance and the left horizontal tail fin forces by the -89 balance.

I always checked each metric surface for integrity after each run, and every time I found the left horizontal had some slop in it. It could be moved back and forth easily, and I had the model mechanics tighten it after each run.

The model mechanics thought I was wiggling the horizontal too hard and making it loose, so I came in after one run and found a sign with a big red circle saying, "NO BILL" on the tail. They wouldn't let me touch the model. I complained to the test engineer and had the "NO BILL" ban removed. I also had the horizontal tightened again.

A few runs later, I was watching the model run on the TV monitor. The model was at high angle of attack when the left horizontal suddenly rotated 90 degrees to the flow. I yelled, "SHUT DOWN!" and we went in to find the back of the -89 balance was completely twisted around like a corkscrew.

The taper end that fit into the mounting fixture was fitted to receive the roll pins. While the roll pins only extended 0.2 inches into the slots in the balance, the slots were cut all the way through from one side to the other every 90 degrees. 70% of the length of the taper joint was slotted. From the back, it looked like a pie cut into four pieces with a #10 screw hole drilled and tapped down the middle.

There was no strength left to resist any bending, and only about 30% of the taper joint was effective in holding the joint against loads. When it finally failed, the long legs of the taper twisted against the roll pins. This had been the problem I had been fighting all along.

Bob apologized to me, and John, the designer, had all the old -89 balances destroyed and a new set (five or six) made in the shop. This time, the roll pin slots were only about 0.3 inches deep leaving the whole taper region as one solid block. No more problems with that!

One time, I was in Bob's office, and he began to reminisce about the old days. He recalled coming down the stairs in Plant 1 with a big armload of drawings. He bumped into someone, and they both fell down. The guy he hit apologized and started helping him pick up the drawings.

It was Jack Northrop, the company president.

Bob told me they used to find ways to keep Jack from coming to the wood shop and getting in the way making stuff.

One of our electronic technicians, told me of working in the cockpit of an airplane with his feet up over the seat. He heard someone climb onto the wing and ask, "How's it going." Pete talked as he worked and had the guy hand him wrenches. When he finished and got his head from under the instrument panel, he found Jack Northrop had been handing him wrenches. Jack was that kind of down-to-earth guy.

Then Bob recalled a time when Northrop was developing the YC-123 cargo airplane. The YC-123 had started as a replacement for the Ford Tri-motor as a bush airplane. The Air Force got interested and added requirement after requirement and the plane grew and grew, and so did the costs.

One day as Bob was having lunch in the cafeteria, Jack came in and made an announcement. He said they had put so much into the YC-123 that they could not make the payroll that week. He asked if the engineers would wait for a couple of weeks for their paychecks until they got in a payment.

They all agreed.

Bob said there were tears running down Jack's face as he asked. And I saw tears running down Bob's face as he remembered.

One day, Roy Eversz and I were going through the Space Lab building and saw an empty office full of executive furniture. We had gone past this office several times before and knew it had been unoccupied for weeks. So, we had an idea.

A wonderful, terrible idea!

Bob's office furniture was from the 1940's. We decided, Bob ought to have this furniture. Besides Bob's office was on the third floor. No one ever went all the way up there to see them. No one would ever find out. So when Bob was off work, Roy and I put on our white shop coats, got a couple of clipboards, took several technicians and some hand carts and went furniture shopping.

If you want to steal something, act like you own the place and work in broad daylight. Roy and I acted like supervisors, and we got all that nice maple furniture to the wind tunnel.

The guys lowered Bob's old furniture from the third floor using a crane then hauled up the new furniture while Bob was gone. Bob was amazed and delighted when he returned, but after a few days he got cold feet and made us take it all back. He feared some VP might come up and see Bob had better furniture than he had.

Just trying to keep our boss happy was our main job at Northrop.

Years later, after Roy was dead and Bob had several strokes, I rearranged Bob's furniture again. Again, without Bob's knowledge. Bob had been out recovering from a stroke for months, and I was acting manager. We got word Bob was coming back to work the next week, and I was worried about him negotiating those three flights of steep stairs, especially as he was partially dragging one foot as he walked.

I had all the workbenches removed from the Strain Gage Lab on the first floor and relocated Bob's furniture to set up in the room. I fully expected to get yelled at and have to move everything upstairs again, but Bob settled into his new nest with nary a word. He continued there until he retired.

The Wind Tunnel building had been built with the men's room on the first floor and the ladies' room for the secretary was on the third floor. Bob, Roy and I all had our offices on the third floor. Mine was just outside the lady's room.

After Bob's first stroke, it was hard for Bob to run up and down the stairs too often. Many times, I would hear Carol, our secretary, call out from the bathroom, "Bob. You left the seat up again." She got quite a kick out of it.

We all loved Bob.

Much later, a year or so before Bob retired, I noticed he seemed to snap and even argue more often with me. I thought he was just getting old and maybe hurting a little.

While Bob was recovering from another stroke, I was acting manager. Fred Peitzman was our second level manager. Fred came into Bob's office for something and I pulled him aside.

"Fred, I know I'm in consideration to replace Bob when he retires. But I just want you to know if I get any sense that you or anyone has forced or pressured him to retire, don't depend on me to take over. I won't do it until Bob is really ready to retire."

Fred said, "But what if Bob just can't keep up or get around to do his job?"

"I'll be his legs and feet and his eyes and ears. I'll run around places for him. But that old man has more knowledge about Northrop and wind tunnels than any ten of us, and we need him."

Later I noticed Bob seemed less suspicious of me, and I realized Bob's secretary, Anna, must have overheard my talk with Fred. I figure Bob must have been thinking that I wanted to take his job.

I did, but never like that.

Mory was a technician who used to give Bob a hard time. One time, Mory came back from a wind tunnel trip with a box of Army C-rations.

"Bob, we just gotta get more per-diem in these trips."

Bob got even though with Mory. We had a small refrigerator in the Strain Gage Lab where everyone kept their brown bag lunches.

Bob made a regular habit of rummaging through the bags to find something he liked. His usual favorites were Mory's sandwiches, which often disappeared before lunch. Mory finally began bringing an extra sandwich for Bob to steal.

A guy's gotta eat.

One day when my office was on the first floor of the wind tunnel building, I watched as the door opened a crack, a hand reached in and grabbed an apple off my desk. Then the door closed. A few seconds later the door opened again, and the arm returned the apple to my desk—minus one bite! Bob Lucas had struck again.

There was an old Christmas tradition at our wind tunnel, one that existed long before I started working there. Any manager or engineer who went into the Model Shop at Christmastime wearing a tie would be grabbed by a huge model mechanic and his tie would be cut off and pinned to the bulletin board. There were usually a couple of ties there from Vice-Presidents and high-level managers.

One year, Dick came in with his tie booby-trapped. He ran a heavy coat hanger wire inside his tie and ran a wire down his sleeve to a little "Christmas present" in his hand.

The "Christmas present" box contained a battery and an old Ford spark coil. For you youngsters who never had the delight of playing with a Ford coil, it had a vibrator to interrupt the battery current continually to produce a spark about an inch and a half long. Playing with things like Ford coils helped lead me to a career in electrical engineering.

Dick showed us his plan, and we all followed him to the Model Shop to watch the fun. Chris, the big mechanic, grabbed Dick to hold him while someone cut off the tie.

Just as the scissors reached the tie, Dick pushed the button on the "Christmas present," half electrocuting the poor guy.

Dick was getting as good as he gave, because he electrocuted himself too. The guy yelled, cursed and dropped the scissors. Chris continued to hold Dick until the guy came back with rubber gloves and large metal shears.

Dick's electric tie went onto the bulletin board with the others.

Later, after many good laughs, I was playing with Dick's "Christmas present" in my office. I always liked making sparks or "blowing things up." I found the weight of the box was just enough to hold down the button switch and keep the Ford coil running.

I had an awful, wonderful idea.

I took a length of wire and connected it between the doorknob and the coil. I held the wooden door open and pressed the box down on the switch to start the Ford coil. Then I slipped out leaving the room empty and the doorknob "hot."

I waited in the room just down the hall for someone to come and go into our office. Just my luck, it was Bob Lucas. He grabbed the door and jerked back into the Calibration Lab across the hall.

Such language!

He went across the hall, slammed the door open, ripped off the wire and tossed the "Christmas present" into the trash can. "If I ever get my hands on the #@$%%@#&^* who did this…"

Bob went to his grave never knowing who had booby-trapped that door. Don't tell him—I hope to see him again someday.

Three weeks after Bob first made me a lead engineer along with Roy Eversz, Bob got sick and was absent for a month. Roy's appendix ruptured, and he was out of work for several weeks also. Suddenly, with little experience leading men, I was running the whole department alone.

I decided I would take control and make the necessary decisions even though I didn't know much about some of the projects our department was working on. That meant I would have to get up to speed fast.

Our group had about eight technicians who built all the electronic equipment needed to operate the research flight simulators. These were used to develop the flight controls for the new aircraft Northrop was competing for.

Roy and Bob had been handling everything on this large project, so I had the technicians building it, and the engineers who had designed the electronics filled me in so I could make the necessary decisions and order the equipment needed.

There was a test being run at night in the Northrop 2x2 supersonic wind tunnel. Wind tunnel tests were supported by a test engineer who oversaw the entire test and ensured the proper model configurations and test conditions were tested.

A technician from the Operations Group maintained and ran the wind tunnel and air compressors and helped with model changes. An Instrumentation Group technician ran the data systems and helped with model changes.

Figure 3: Northrop 2 x 2-foot supersonic wind tunnel. The window is for viewing the test section. This tunnel is run using 3000 psi air and runs last about 45 seconds.

I came in one morning to find the test engineer on this test was complaining the entire test crew had never returned from lunch the night before. This was big trouble!

You cannot out walk off work in the middle of a shift!

I fretted all day about how to chew out our instrumentation technician. He was an older, very worldly guy who had been everywhere and done everything. I was just a green-behind-the-ears kid.

As soon as he came in, I cornered him and found they had all gotten mad at the test engineer (who could sometimes be a jerk— I got mad at him a few times myself) and just left after lunch.

"Sam," I said (I'll call him Sam), "you just can't do that. You'll get fired. Besides we still have to get this test data."

It seems that the test engineer had sat down on the control console during a run and sat on the "Emergency Shutdown" button and ruined a run.

"Sam" could have run all over me, but he just sheepishly said, "Ok. I'll never do it again."

And he never did.

Things went relatively smoothly after that and Bob eventually returned. Boy was I ever glad.

CHAPTER 2

Balance Calibration Techniques or "Oh, My Aching Back"

Balances are used to measure the aerodynamic forces acting on the wind tunnel model. The main balance resolves the force into six components: Normal Force(up direction), Side Force, Axial Force (toward the tail), Pitching Moment, Yawing Movement and Rolling Moment.

Smaller balances are used to measure five, three, or one component of the force. They are often used to measure the forces on stores, bombs, tail surfaces, control surfaces, etc.

All balances are six-component balances.

All force balances are affected by all six forces, even if only one or three are measured. Forces applied in the other directions still affect the output of the gages being measured. These are referred to as interactions.

When all six components are measured, these interactions can be measured and compensated for. If fewer forces are measured, the interactions cannot be compensated for and the accuracy of the balance is reduced.

All these balances use strain gages to convert the forces to electrical outputs. They

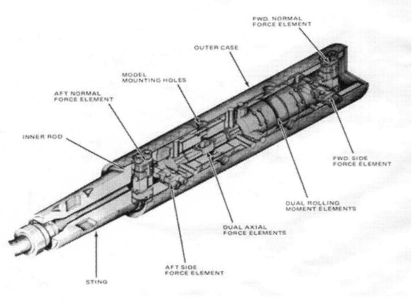

Figure 4: Able balance

are very precisely built to concentrate each force component in the area where the strain gages are cemented to the balance.

There are two types of balances used: force balances and moment balances. Force balances measure the normal forces and side forces at two locations, which allows the total normal and side forces and pitching and yawing moments to be calculated. Drag and rolling moment are measured directly.

Moment balances measure the pitching and yawing moments at two locations, which allow the calculation of total normal and side forces. Drag and rolling moments

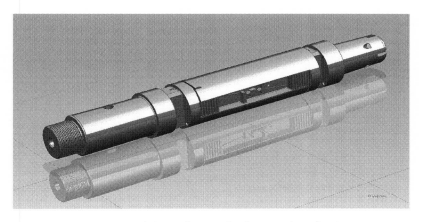

Figure 5: Moment balance. The tapered end is inserted into the sting, which is connected to the support system. The model is slipped over this entire assembly.

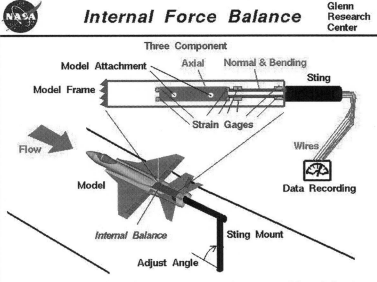

Figure 6: This picture shows the way forces measured are measured through the sting.

are measured directly also.

Many student pilots (and some of their instructors) confuse normal and axial forces on the airplane with lift and drag. They look at pictures which show lift and drag being balanced by gravity and thrust *in level flight*. Then when the aircraft is at an angle of attack, they do not have a name for the upward force which is acting perpendicular to the wings.

Lift is always perpendicular to the wind, and *drag is always in the wind direction, no matter what the angle of attack.*

These balances must be carefully calibrated to relate the electrical outputs to the applied forces. Since they are mechanical systems with slight imperfections, there are interactions between the gages: a force applied at a place which should affect only one component will cause a small electrical output from the other gages. These are accounted for in the matrix used to reduce the data. These balances may be designed to measure between a few pounds to several thousand pounds. Several devices have been developed to make it easier to calibrate large balances.

NASA Ames Research Center uses a hydraulic force multiplier for calibration. Calspan uses a motorized weight tray, which drops down to allow one weight at a time to hang from the balance. Rockwell used a really big, husky guy to lift the weights. At Northrop we used two guys to lift the heavier weights, and one of them was usually me.

The weights are applied in five to ten increments to measure the linearity. The balance used most at Northrop was rated at 2,000 pounds total force. That meant each normal force gage, N1 and N2, had to be loaded in 100-pound increments up to 1,000 pounds in both the positive and negative directions. Before recording the calibration data, each calibration was preloaded to its maximum weight to reduce hysteresis. That

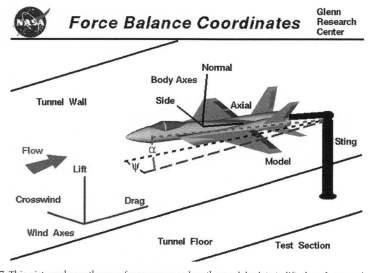

Figure 7: This picture shows the way forces measured on the model relate to lift, drag & crosswind forces.

Figure 8: F5E models being assembled on the calibration stands. The whole assembly can be pitched and rolled. The balance calibration has already been completed. The data system is behind the model.

meant we put 1,000 pounds on, took them off, and put them on again, four times.

You would think that I would have built big muscles doing this—alas no such luck.

Usually as we calibrated a balance, we also measured the angular deflection of the balance and sting system. Each large weight added to the load pan caused a very noticeable droop to the assembly.

Perhaps the most delicate measurement when calibrating a balance is proper leveling of the balance.

The balance is calibrated by mounting a calibration body on the balance. This is a steel, rectangular block which encloses the balance. Its sides are precisely flat and perpendicular to each other. It has pin and screw holes precisely at the place where the gages which measure the forces are located. This way, the weights can be applied directly to each strain gage flexure. Flexures (thin, flexible machined attachments) are used to support the weight pan and allow it to hang straight down.

The procedure goes something like this: To prepared to calibrate the forward normal force, +N1, an adapter for a balance pan was attached to the calibration body at the +N1 location. A very accurate inclinometer is placed on a fixture on the calibration stand to measure the angular deflection of the sting and balance.

My partner and I stand on opposite sides of the balance facing each other. The weights are sitting on a tray on the floor near the end of the balance. The weights are slotted to slide around the shaft of the weight pan. Each weight is lifted, flipped over, and slipped onto the weight pan, until ten 100-pound weights are on the weight pan, applying 1,000 pounds to the balance Normal Force gage.

Then the weight tray is rolled away, a pair of 4x4's placed nearby on the floor and all ten weights are removed from the weight pan and placed on the 4x4s. The balance is leveled using a very accurate bubble level placed on the calibration block and the zero data point is recorded. One 100-pound weight is placed onto then weight pan, the balance is re-leveled, the inclinometer read, and a data point recorded.

This procedure is repeated for each 100-pound weight until all 1,000 pounds are applied. Two data points are recorded at the maximum weight. Then the weights are removed one at a time, recording data at each weight on the way down. In this way, the response of each strain gage is recorded twice, once with increasing load and once with decreasing load. This allows to evaluate both the linearity and hysteresis associated with each gage.

The load pan is now attached at the +N2, aft normal force gage location, and all ten weights applied at this station. Then the weights are applied one-by-one recording the same data as above. The balance is then rolled over 180 degrees in the calibration body, and the N1 and N2 gages calibrated in the negative direction.

Again, the balance is rotated 90 degrees in the calibration body, and the side forces, S1 and S2 are calibrated in both positive and negative directions. Side force gages are usually rated for about half the capacity of the normal force gages.

So far, eight calibrations have been completed and over 12,000 pounds of weights have been hefted around.

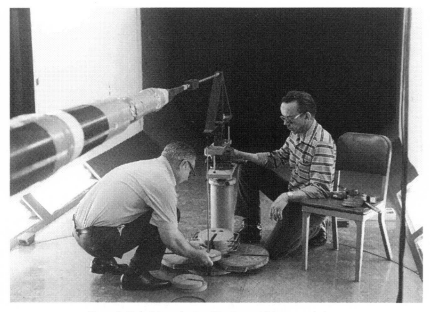

Figure 9: Technicians check-calibrating axial force on a balance
in the 7x10 wind tunnel using the drag calibration flexure.

The roll gages are calibrated by attaching the roll arms to the calibration body with their load pans. The distance between the pans is measured, and the number of weights needed to apply the maximum roll torque is calculated. These are usually in the ten or twenty pound range.

Half the weights are placed on the right roll arm and half on the other arm. For the positive calibration, all the weights are placed on the right load pan for a moment to preload it, then half is returned to the other pan. The balance is leveled, and the zero data point recorded.

One weight is moved from the left pan to the right, the balance re-leveled and a data point recorded. This is repeated as each weight is moved and returned back until the full calibration is completed.

Then the negative side is preloaded, and the calibration completed.

Lastly, the axial force gage is calibrated using the drag calibration flexure. This "walking beam" must be carefully aligned directly in front of the balance so the calibration forces are applied directly along the axis of the balance.

The push rod must be adjusted left and right using straight edge rulers. The height is adjusted so the connecting rod is level when the balance and the top of the calibration rig is level.

Everything must be kept level throughout the calibration procedure.

Enough weights, usually 100 to 200 pounds, the capacity of the axial force gages, are placed on the two load pans, one half on each pan. After recording data system calibrations and zeros, a weight is moved from one load pan to then other. This causes a load of twenty pounds to be applied to the balance, ten pounds off the one pad and ten pounds onto the other.

This process is repeated for each load, up and down, until all weights are back where they started, and zero load is applied.

The whole process is repeated in the other direction to calibrate the balance in the negative direction.

After the entire calibration is completed, you should have recorded twelve good calibration runs. All this data is then processed by the computer to produce a 6x6 matrix, which can be used to accurately calculate all the forces and moments the wind tunnel model produces during the test.

This entire operation can usually be completed in one eight-hour day by two people, but you will both go home quite tired!

CHAPTER 3

Bubble Packs or Which Way is Up?

I didn't invent or develop the bubble packs we used at Northrop to level the wind tunnel models, but Roy Eversz and I did make them more practical and accurate.

It is very important to level wind tunnel models accurately since this is the point from which the pitch angle of the model is measured. Much of the data taken is plotted against pitch angle. Also, it is important to start from the same pitch angle from test-to-test and tunnel-to-tunnel in order to compare data.

Most wind tunnels use leveling plates to level the model before testing. This leveling plate is attached to the top of the model in an area that has been machined flat to be level with the Horizontal Reference Line (HRL) against which the model is machined. A precision bubble level is then placed on the pad when the model is mounted in the tunnel, and the pitch system is used to level the model. The pitch readouts are then set to read zero before the test starts.

Sometimes three legs are used to support the leveling plate, and the pads where the legs attach and the legs themselves must be carefully machined to be sure the plate is level with the HRL.

At Northrop we usually ran our models upright and inverted to measure any flow angularity in the tunnel. This would mean the leveling pad had to be attached to the bottom of the model also. This left too many places for an error to occur in this crucial leveling procedure. Our guys came up with a better way to level wind tunnel models: the electrolytic bubble pack.

Northrop started using bubble packs to level models before I got involved with wind tunnel testing. The system utilized little bubble levels manufactured by Hamlin Corporation. These were like the hardware store bubble levels except they were filled with an electrolytic chemical, which conducted electricity and had three wires molded into the glass. One wire ran the length of the bubble and the two others protruded a little way through the glass into the conductive liquid.

As the bubble is tilted side-to-side the resistance between the common lead and the other leads varied, one leg increasing and the other leg decreasing. These resistance changes are measured using a Wheatstone bridge circuit.

Level is determined when the resistances are equal.

Alternating current is used to keep chemical changes in the electrodes balanced. The bridge output is amplified and displayed on a panel meter which indicates level when the meter reads the lowest value or "null point."

We often ran models upright, inverted, and +/- 90 degree roll angle (wings vertical) in our tunnel. The model had to be leveled in both pitch and roll for each rotation angle. This required eight bubbles, two for each 90 degree position.

They were all mounted on an aluminum base about two inches long by one inch wide and one inch tall. Each bubble could be adjusted by loosening a screw on its mounting plate and pushing one end up or down. This adjustment was touchy because the bubbles were very sensitive.

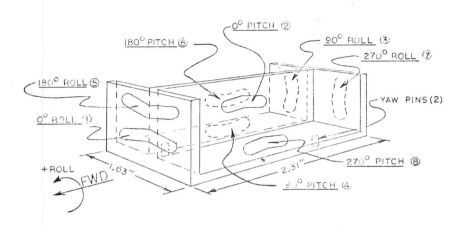

Figure 9: Sketch of Bubble Package showing orientation of electrolytic bubbles

My introduction to bubble packs was when I had to get one ready for the A9A test at Ames Research Center. The Model Shop rigged the model on a dummy balance and leveled it so that I could adjust the bubbles to read level when the model was level.

The bubbles for upright and plus and minus 90 degrees were touchy but not too difficult. Laying on the dirty shop floor on my back reaching up into the deep nose of that model and trying to tweak those two inverted bubbles was a real pain, literally!

There had to be a better way than this! After the A9A test, I started to work on developing a new method. They say necessity is the mother of invention. I say laziness is the father. There had to be an easier way to do this!

Roy Eversz and I talked about the problem. This method was difficult, not very accurate, and not too repeatable from test-to-test. We decided to calibrate the bubble packs by mounting them on a block on our calibration stand so we had a large test block modified to attach a bubble pack to it.

We could more easily adjust each bubble to level at an easy-to-reach level in a well-lit room. We leveled the calibration block with the same Fell levels we used to level Task balances. The levels were accurate to eight arc-seconds.

We soon realized our old calibration block wasn't that flat, so we had a more accurate block machined and sent to the Northrop Standards Lab to ensure the sides were flat and accurately 90 degrees to each other.

Since this was a reference measurement, Roy and I felt we should strive for accuracies five to ten times that to which the model was built, which was usually plus or minus one minute. Ten times that tolerance is 0.1 minute, or six arc-seconds. Our eight arc-second Fell levels were right in that range. Later we graduated to Higler-Watts optical inclinometers, which were accurate to one arc-second, and cost $14,000 at that time.

The Model Shop was hard pressed to keep up with our increased accuracies. For this new system to work, the place where the bubble packs mounted on the models would have to be machined to be accurately parallel to the model HRL since the bubbles could no longer be adjusted individually to compensate for any errors. This meant it needed the support of the Test Engineering group, so Roy and I went to Fred Pietzman. With his help we all came up with a system that would be more accurate and repeatable than anything else used in the industry.

First, the bubble pack for each model would be mounted on a location which would never change angle relative to the HRL of the model. That meant it would not be mounted to the nose or any other part of the model that could be removed. The balance block, the central core of the model around which the model is built, was the preferred location. This would ensure the reference level of the model would be consistent test-to-test, year after year. Also, if a bubble pack went bad during a test, it could be instantly replaced by another one which was already calibrated.

Second, Roy and I would have liked to have had the mounting pad for the bubble packs in the model be five to ten times more accurate than the rest of the model tolerances, but this would not have been practical. We finally agreed with Fred on a set of tolerances: +/- 0.5 minute in pitch and +/- 3 minutes in roll and yaw.

The mounting surface would have to be carefully precision ground to these tolerances. Then we would measure exactly where the nose pointed when the bubble pack indicated level and record the actual rigging of the model which should never change. If it was not within the tolerance, it would have to be ground again.

We got a lot of complaints from the shop guys over these new tolerances. It was always "right on" or "dead on" when we went to the shop to check the rigging of the model. After a few rejects and reworks and with much arguing, the shop got the technique down and turned out excellent models with very accurate bubble pack set ups.

To check the rigging of the models, we also had to get the shop to accurately level one of their Microflat granite tables and to quit using it as an anvil, chipping it. Once we got the system working smoothly, all went fine, and everyone was happy.

We always used bubble packs at the Northrop wind tunnels and found them to be very reliable and accurate. The people at other wind tunnels however were suspicious of them and still wanted us to provide a leveling plate when we tested at their facilities. We learned to level the model using the bubble pack then adjust the level plate to agree with the bubble pack. This made bubble packs more acceptable to others.

But to further convince others, my boss, Bob Lucas, assigned me the task of testing bubble packs and writing a technical paper on them.

I measured the accuracy and repeatability of several bubble packs and measured the effects of air pressure, tilt angle, and temperature on them. Also, since wind tunnels generate a lot of heat, I carefully examined their temperature characteristics. This seemed to be the area most other engineers questioned.

Several other tunnels had examined Hamlin bubbles and found them unreliable, but they did not use them in the same manner we did.

I found the null point of the bubbles was very accurate, reliable and repeatable. The slope of the curve leading to that null, however, varied with temperature, becoming steeper as temperature increased.

Thus, a reading of thirty on the meter might mean an angle of one arc-minute at 70 degrees Fahrenheit and 1.5 arc-minutes at 150 degrees.

The question that always came up during a test was, "How close is close enough?"

I could only reply, "Only the minimum reading is close enough. Try again."

Or someone would ask, "Are we nose high or nose low?"

I'd shrug, "I don't know."

This study resulted in my writing two technical papers: one for the Supersonic Tunnel Association (STA) and another for the Instrument Society of America (ISA).

With these papers in hand to add credibility to our use of bubble packs, I went to several pretest meetings at wind tunnels such as Calspan and AEDC to sell them on how we used bubble packs. When they compared the results of the bubble packs with the leveling plates, they accepted them and allowed us to use them for our tests there.

They were much faster to use than running into the tunnel and putting on a leveling plate, but to the best of my knowledge, no other company or facility ever used bubble packs very often.

We had a real problem when testing at Calspan's 8-foot Transonic tunnel. The bubble pack was way more accurate than their support system. It was almost impossible to level the model to the arc-second range. They couldn't get a good null setting.

At the AEDC 16-foot Transonic tunnel, we had no problem leveling the model to the bubble pack. Then we would go into the tunnel and check the leveling plate with a bubble or inclinometer.

A tunnel technician would check the level and tell us it was off by some amount. Then he would get off the ladder, and I would climb up to the model. The model would be eight feet high. I'd check the bubble level on the leveling plate and turn it 180 degrees around. If it was accurate, it would give the same reading when reversed, but usually, the bubble would bounce to one side. I would show it to the technician and send him off mumbling to get another level. We had great success there with the bubble packs.

In our own Northrop 7x10 Foot Low Speed tunnel, we had a very nice support system which had been designed by our Design Group and built by our Model Shop. It was hydraulically operated and controlled by an electronic servo system that had been designed by our flight simulator Design Group and wired and built by our own Instrumentation Group, which had also built all the electronic systems for the simulators.

This support system could pitch the model from -15 to +90 degrees. It usually was operated in the "BSO" (Balance System Origin) mode where the model pitched about a point in the middle of the tunnel (the BSO point). But sometimes, the model could be moved vertically in the tunnel while set to any pitch angle in its range. This allowed us to test in ground effect near the tunnel floor.

This system was so smooth and accurate that setting to bubble pack accurately was easy.

CHAPTER 4

Laminar Flow Control and Hot Wires

In the early 1960's, Northrop was testing the X-21 Laminar Flow Control airplane. This was a concept first developed by the Germans during World War II and brought to Northrop by Dr. Werner Pfenninger, who had come to the U.S. after the war.

As air flows over the wing of an airplane, the air next to the surface slows down due to friction. This then slows down the next layer of air, and this boundary layer gets thicker as the air flows to the back of the wing.

At first this air flows smoothly causing little drag to the airplane, but after a while the boundary layer becomes unstable and turns turbulent, causing increased drag. Many aircraft carefully shape the airfoil to keep the flow laminar over more of the wing, but Dr. Finninger had a better idea.

His plan was to suck off the boundary layer before it could become turbulent and repeat this sucking again and again as the air flow progressed over the wing. He accomplished this through tiny holes and slots, two to three thousandths of an inch wide which ran from the wing root to the tip. These slots were spaced about every inch at the front of the wing to every couple of inches over the top pf the wing. These openings were ducted to a vacuum pump in the fuselage.

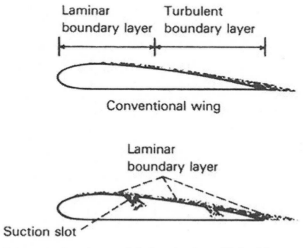

Figure 11: Using suction in a wing to suck the boundary layer off before it becomes turbulent.

Maintaining laminar flow is sometimes a tricky business. Just a slight speck of dirt or unevenness can trip the flow to turbulent.

Dr. Pfenninger believed his technique of sucking off the boundary layer could reduce drag and improve performance by more than fifteen to twenty percent. To prove his theory, he got a contract from the Air Force to have Northrop to convert an RB-66 bomber to the X-21 test airplane by replacing the wings with his laminar flow control wings.

When the performance improvement turned out less than predicted, we got involved to find out why. Were the slots in the wing wide enough to suck off enough air? Did noise come out of the slots and trip the flow?

We performed tests placing hot wire anemometers down inside the slots. Hot wire anemometers are tiny wires such as platinum wires one thousandth of an inch (0.001") or less in diameter and one tenth of an inch long, welded onto the tips of a pair of needles. The wire is heated electrically, and the power required to heat it is a measure of the air speed flowing over it, just like the fan on your radiator in your car improves the cooling.

Figure 12: X-21A aircraft used to demonstrate the advantages of using boundary layer suction to reduce turbulence and reduce drag. The span-wise slots can be seen on the wings.

Another advantage of hot wires is that they are so small they cool very rapidly and can follow the fluctuations of turbulence and measure its level. These small wires were positioned in and above the slots using micrometer positioners.

One thing noticed during these tests was noise from the vacuum pumps might be working up the duct and out through the slots, tripping the flow to turbulent. This led to a series of tests to simulate and measure this phenomenon in wind tunnels at Northrop and the Ames Research Center in Mountain View, CA.

We built a full-scale section of the wing about seven feet long and mounted twenty five precision microphones along the ducts in it. We also placed hi-fi speaker drivers in the end of each of the seven ducts in the wing. Other microphones were mounted on the wing surface, and hot wires were used to measure the turbulence. Thus, we could blast white noise or discrete frequencies up then ducts and find which kinds of noise was causing turbulence to determine how to fix it.

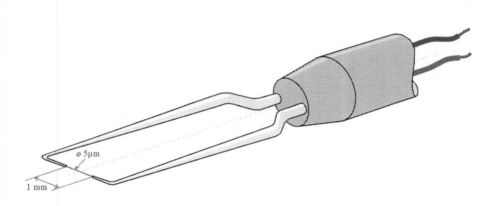

Figure 13: Hot wire anemometer

The test at Ames was in the 10-foot Pressure Tunnel which can run at five times atmospheric pressure. This allows testing at higher Reynold's Numbers, which better matches flight conditions. Reynold's Number is directly related to the transition to turbulent flow.

This wide range of pressures required special techniques and equipment to calibrate the microphones and speakers. We built a special pressure chamber in which to calibrate the equipment and summarized the calibration results in a special report. The tests were successful and showed fan noise caused less turbulence than expected.

One other possible cause of the greater turbulent areas on the wing was uneven distribution of the suction in some areas of the wing. Were we getting enough air flowing in through the slots in some areas? The air flow from various areas was controlled by remotely operated "flapper valves" located in the ducts which led to various sections of the wing.

Each slot ran the length of the wing from root to tip and was cut through the outer aluminum skin. Bonded directly under the slot was a row of fiberglass chambers about four inches long and a half inch wide, placed end to end. In the end of each chamber was a small nozzle designed to restrict the amount of air to be sucked in through that area of the slot.

The next slot back on the wing was about an inch or two away from the first slot, just far enough from the first to allow another row of chambers to be glued there. Inside the wing, three or four of the ducts with their chambers were covered for several feet with a long fiberglass box or duct, which connected them together to a larger duct eventually leading back to the vacuum pump at the wing root. This duct system was sort of like the branches of a tree leading back to the trunk. There was a flapper valve located where each duct connected to a larger duct.

The designers calculated how much air should be sucked off from each area of the wing, but there was no provision for measuring how much air was really flowing in each duct. The valves could control the flow in each duct, but what was really happening?

A bunch of us engineers were called to a meeting to discuss this problem. Someone asked, "Could we just put a toaster wire in each flapper valve, like a hot wire, and measure the air flow?" There was concern the air flow was very unevenly distributed in the ducts and valves.

Most other engineers faced with a question like this grabbed their slide rules and started calculating. Me, I was just too green and dumb to calculate the answer. I simply said, "I don't know, but we can try." And that was how I got into an interesting series of tests and a few problems.

The first test was to check out the concept. A hot wire anemometer works by heating a small wire electrically and measuring the amount of heat transferred from the wire to the air. It takes electrical power to heat the wire to a certain temperature. The faster the air blows over the wire, the colder the wire gets, and more power is required to heat the wire to the same temperature. How do we measure the wire temperature? We measure the resistance of the wire using a Wheatstone bridge, which accurately compares the resistance of the wire to a known resistance. To make the system more sensitive to flow changes, we therefore want to use wire material which has a large change of resistance with temperature.

To see if this idea would work, I looked over the tables of resistivity and found iron had one of the greatest temperature coefficients of resistivity. Pure iron wire of accurate diameter was readily available in thermocouple wire which we used a lot in instrumentation.

I had the Model Shop build several four-foot-long wooden ducts: round, triangular, and rectangular with openings four or five inches across. I used 22-gage thermocouple wire, which I stripped off the insulation and stretched across each duct.

I also built a Wheatstone bridge circuit that allowed me to balance the bridge cold then re-balance it by heating the hot wire to a percentage above the cold resistance by heating the wire with an electrical current. I used a nanovoltmeter to determine an accurate bridge null and a 20-ampere, adjustable power supply to heat the wire.

Air flow was supplied by suction from our labs "secondary" pumping system to which the ducts were connected. This system included a calibrated metering orifice to measure the weight flow rate of the air. With the air flowing at the desired rate, I would balance the bridge cold, which determined the wire's resistance at the air temperature. Then, I would select an "overheat ratio," such as 1.10, and crank up the voltage of the power supply until the nanovoltmeter read zero, indicating the wire had been heated to the proper temperature. I recorded the current from the power supply using a digital DC ammeter. The orifice meter measurements were also recorded. This produced a single data point.

I increased the air flow rate and repeated the entire procedure for the next data point. As air flow increased, the amount of current indicated the increased power needed to heat the wire to the same temperature.

In this way I could calibrate the wires versus airflow for all the ducts, each of which had screwed up airflow: faster at one end of the wire, slower at the other end. The worst case I tested was with half of the entrance of the round duct blocked off with a piece of plywood.

If I could process the data in such a way that it all produced a single calibration curve, I would have an instrument capable of measuring airflow accurately, even if the flow was badly screwed up.

I found the data from all these ducts agreed within 10%— a very good correlation under the circumstances. This was very successful. It seemed possible an instrument could be devised capable of measuring the weight flow in screwed up airflow with reasonable accuracy.

Great! Full speed ahead.

Upon examining the wires used in the test, I discovered the leading edge of the iron wires were badly corroded— a result of Los Angeles smog. I would have to use wire of a different material for the next phase. I still needed a wire with a large change of resistance with temperature but more corrosion resistant.

I selected titanium. Titanium thermocouple wire is readily available. The diameter of thermocouple wire is accurately controlled, which is an important parameter.

The next phase of the development testing was to simulate the conditions encountered by the aircraft in flight testing. I was given an actual flapper valve, such as was installed in the X-21 aircraft. Also, I would have to match the low density and very cold air encountered in high altitude flight.

The shop built a wooden duct which would connect the flapper valve to a pipe, which was connected to a four-inch orifice flow meter attached to the Inlet and Duct Facility "secondary" suction system.

The upstream end of the flapper valve was attached to another wooden duct, which connected through quarter inch steel tubing to the facility's 3,000 psi high pressure air supply system. I controlled the air flow rate with a hand-controlled needle valve and cooled the incoming high-pressure air with a coil of quarter inch stainless steel tubing immersed in a five-gallon bucket of liquid nitrogen.

Liquid nitrogen was available by hauling a special Dewar flask, which was a little larger than a Radio Flyer wagon. The LN2 was stored a couple of hundred feet from the I&D Facility at the Engineering Test Labs. This test setup allowed me to make measurements in a vacuum to below two inches of mercury and −90 degrees Fahrenheit, matching a cold day at 90,000 feet altitude.

I used the same hot wire control system which I had used in the previous test. I installed the tungsten wire diagonally across the exit area of the flapper valve. There was a timing problem with my test. Another engineer was conducting a different test in the other test cell and needed the same secondary suction system. He was obnoxiously insisting his test had priority over my test, using this situation to force management to make a high-level decision.

First, I was cleared to test, then he was. This back and forth was really irritating my manager at that time, Harry Graves. It made me a little nervous to be ticking off my boss like this, so I went to the second level manager and asked him how to handle the problem. He said, "You do what you need to run your test properly, and I'll take care of Harry."

The compromise we came up with was that I would run from 5 a.m. until noon, then the other guy would run from noon to the end of the day.

Northrop used a number of little Daihatsu two-cycle, tricycle utility cars as utility vehicles. One manager in the Aerosciences Lab controlled the keys for the ones we used. I had two assistants for this test and 5 a.m. each morning, we would find ourselves stealing one of these Daihatsu's.

We tied the pull bar of the Dewar flask to the license plate holder and towed it to the test labs, filling it from the main LN2 storage tank. As we filled it, the entire area around the test labs engulfed with the fog that it created. We would tow the Dewar back to the rear of the I&D cell, fill the five-gallon can with LN2 and start testing.

We would repeat this LN2 run each time we depleted our LN2 reserve.

At noon, during everyone else's lunch, we would return the Daihatsu to the Daihatsu pool. Then I would analyze data the rest of the day. The manager who owned the Daihatsu's got very mad because the license plate holder (the Daihatsu's were not licensed) of one of his new Daihatsu's was being bent out of shape. He never did figure out my little larceny.

That was a fun test. The floor of the test cell was littered with pieces of rubber hose, cherries, leather, and any thing we could freeze in LN2 and shatter into a thousand pieces.

King's Law states the square of the current, I, is proportional to the square root of the air velocity, V. This is the formula generally utilized by users of hot wire systems.

This formula did not work well for me over the wide range of temperatures and velocities needed. I had to go back to basic heat transfer thermodynamics to get good data correlation over the wide range of variables.

When I first tried to find a formula to represent the data, I plotted it in different ways, and my data looked like the Milky Way on a clear night. Imagine trying to figure the best fit for straight line through the stars of the Milky Way!

Finally, I got a good data fit by plotting the Nusselt number, which contains the square of the current, versus the Reynolds number, which is proportional to the square root of the mass flow rate. These are both basic parameters of heat transfer. I even threw in the Prandtl number for good measure. The standard deviation of the data was less than 10%. There were over a thousand data points. Success!

Most aerospace companies hire well-known research consultants to use their names to get government contracts. One such fellow who worked for Northrop was Dr. Bogdanoff from Princeton University.

They asked him to review my research. He said, "I usually recommend different ways to continue research on a project, but in this case, I recommend that you patent this instrument and get it on the market. California is constructing the aqueduct system to bring water to Los Angeles. This would be ideal for measuring flow throughout the system."

That never happened.

I never got a cent from it at all. But years later, I was consulting with Computer Science Corporation and called Dr. Bogdanoff to see if he would consult with CSC on a proposal to build a system to control the operation of the Aeropropulsion System Test Facility at the Arnold Engineering Development Center in Tennessee. He declined because the Air Force had already contracted with him to work on the same project.

CHAPTER 5

Hot Gas Ingestion Testing

In the 1960's a new Ph.D., came to us with an unusual challenge. He wanted us to make special thermocouples which would rapidly respond to transient air temperature changes. He was making a study of jet engines losing thrust from ingesting short bursts of hot air. This was especially a problem for Vertical Take Off and Landing (VTOL) Aircraft.

Previous studies used thermocouples made from 26- or 28-gauge wire, often with a large weld bead at the junction. This engineer believed their response was too slow to accurately measure the peak temperatures of short bursts of hot air. He wanted to make thermocouples by butt-welding thermocouple wires one to three thousandths of an inch diameter. We had one technician who became our expert in welding two pieces of tiny thermocouple wire together under a microscope. He would then expose about a quarter inch of a pair of 26-gauge thermocouple wires from their sheath and weld these tiny wires across the quarter inch gap between them.

The 26-gauge wire is sixteen-thousandths inch diameter, sturdy enough to hold the thermocouples in place, yet the tiny wires would respond very quickly to rapid changes in air temperature. He made several thermocouples of 0.001-, 0.002- and 0.003-inch diameter wire so that we could compare the data to be certain the thermocouples were accurately following the air temperature changes. The thermocouple probes resembled hot wire anemometer probes.

The test cell in the I&D (Inlet and Duct) facility was nearly filled by the circular flat plate model. This had rows of static pressure taps extending radially from the center to the edge. Above it was mounted two one-inch jet nozzles which could be moved vertically and closer or father apart from each other. The air supplied to the nozzles could be as hot as 300 degrees Fahrenheit and as much as 100 psi.

Small, simulated inlets were attached to the nozzles. These had three tiny thermocouples installed in each of them and were supplied with suction from out secondary suction pump.

The idea was hot air from the twin jets would blast onto the flat table and some of it would swirl around and be sucked into the inlets. Those short bursts of hot air would be measured by the thermocouples.

The thermocouple data would be recorded on oscillographs, the old-style method of recording dynamic data using light beams projected off tiny mirrors onto photo sensitive paper which would be developed later. Up to fifty channels of data could be recorded this way. Lyle Washburn, our former flight test engineer was an expert on oscillographs. Pressure data was measured on manometers in the control room.

Our Ph.D. had an assortment of paddle wheels, vanes, tuft probes and pressure rakes to help him understand how the air was flowing.

To run a test, Warren Adams, the systems operator, would don ear muffs and stand in the back corner of the test cell to operate the two valves that supplied hot air to the nozzles. Our Ph.D. probed the flow around the nozzles and inlets, telling Lyle and me when to take data. We recorded the manometers and ran the oscillograph. This guy had a bad habit of feeling the air with his hand and getting it sucked into the little inlets, breaking the tiny thermocouples. That kept our technician busy repairing thermocouples.

One time during a test, our Ph.D. placed a pressure rake too close to the jets and blew the water manometer board over the top. He left the area, and I came into the cell to find the rake peeing out six little streams of green liquid onto the floor.

Another time, one of the pressure-taps on the table was plugged with something and before we could stop him, he grabbed an air hose and tried to blow it out with shop air. I heard mercury hitting the ceiling in the control room before we could stop him.

Later, this Ph.D. became one of Northrop's best engineers, an expert on engine inlet and duct systems. We worked on many successful projects together and laughed at his earlier mistakes. At one point, he wanted to inject water into the hot jets to produce steam and visualize the flow patterns. That meant the water would have to be pumped into the jets at higher than the 100 psi air that was flowing. Warren Adams installed a water pump, and we got ready to run.

I watched Warren standing in the corner of the test cell through the control room window. He turned on the air, and it started to howl. Then he turned on the water and instantly disappeared in a cloud of steam.

It took him about twenty seconds to turn off the air and water. He and the Ph.D. emerged from the steam cloud totally drenched and dripping water.

"Maybe a little too much water, Warren?"

Next time, they cut down the water flow with a valve, and it worked just fine, but after all these years, I can still see Warren disappearing into the cloud with a funny look on his face.

This guy's testing proved previous inlet temperature measurements responded too slowly to temperature changes, and he created a better technique for measuring that data. At that time, there was much interest in V/STOL aircraft, and hot gas ingestion was a problem, so this test led to several other larger tests for us all.

A Lot of Noise at Ames

This Ph.D.'s next project was a full-scale VTOL engine test which would be run at NASA Ames Research Center in Mountain View, CA. We built a model which simulated a type of VTOL aircraft and measured the hot gases ingested into the inlets using Gordon's fast response thermocouples.

The model had five jet engines mounted vertically in the fuselage plus two engines mounted horizontally in the rear like a twin jet airplane but with the exhausts turned down using bent nozzles.

Lyle Washburn, with his flight test experience, would be the main instrumentation engineer on this project while I assisted him with some of the preparations.

This particular test had several unique challenges. There were over two-hundred fifty thermocouples on this model. Each had to be connected to the control room over two-hundred fifty feet away. Everything was located near the Navy's Moffett Field end of the base, near the 100-megawatt radar. This was likely to cause interference with our instrumentation, especially with those long lead wires.

Figure 14: Ames hot gas ingestion test with 7 full-scale engines

Long lead wires for thermocouples are difficult because the wires must be made of metals compatible with the thermocouple material or they will cause measurement errors. Also, these wires need to be shielded to reduce noise pickup.

Lyle and I wanted to purchase several racks of high-quality instrumentation amplifiers for this job at about $200 for each channel. There would be over a hundred channels.

That was a lot of money, so the project managers went shopping for a cheaper approach. The instrumentation people in our flight test group suggested using operational amplifiers, just a small electronic chip, costing $35 each, and sent us a couple of samples along with a circuit diagram of how to use them.

One of our technicians wired up the operational amplifiers, and we prepared 250-foot thermocouple lead wires and thermocouples to simulate the system we would have at Ames. We feared that much wire would be an antenna for interference from all the Ames equipment, including their 100-megawatt radar system. We also had a couple of the Ectron amplifiers Lyle and I proposed to use.

We connected the whole system in the I&D test cell and monitored the outputs of the four amplifiers on oscilloscopes. The two inexpensive operational amplifier systems were picking up some intermittent noise which lasted a few seconds, then nothing for a minute or two.

The more expensive amplifiers showed no interference.

I watched this noise for a while then got an idea.

I grabbed a headset from our intercom system and wired the headphones into one of the operational amplifiers. In a minute I heard, "Cessna 52 Juliet, cleared for take-off." The Northrop wind tunnels and test cells are located adjacent to the Hawthorne airport. Clearly, the inexpensive operational amplifiers were not going to work near the radar and other noise sources at Ames if they were picking up the Hawthorne control tower. We ordered the Ectron amplifiers and had Warren Tribble and Bob Hobbs mount and wire them for the test.

I stayed home while Lyle and a couple of our technicians spent most of the next six months at Ames. They came home most weekends by proving it was cheaper to check out of the motel and fly back than staying all weekend.

The test lasted longer than expected because the noise from running seven jet engines was so great they were restricted in the times they could test.

Again, the fast response thermocouples showed there was a greater problem with hot gas ingestion than previously thought. As a result, Gordon acquired another contract for further testing.

The Praying Mantis Test

The next test in this series was a scale model test to determine hot gas ingestion as the model rose from the ground at different rates. The model had a couple of simulated inlets connected to a suction system and a couple of jet nozzles fed by hot, high pressure air.

The model's vertical motion was controlled hydraulically, and the whole mechanism was suspended by heavy 12-inch pipe sloping 45 degrees from our hypersonic tunnel's pebble bed heater to thirty feet above the center of the parking lot.

The parking lot between the model shop, the I&D facility, and the Hypersonic/ Supersonic Wind Tunnel buildings was filled with a raised plywood platform ground plane, which was instrumented with pressure taps and thermocouples.

Again, Lyle handled most of this test.

High pressure air from the pebble bed heater was blasted from the bottom of the model with a terrible roar as the model rose up or down over the ground plane. As we were preparing for this test, my boss, Harry Graves, sent me to find out how much room we had to leave beside the raised platform for fire access. I called the Hawthorne Fire Department and asked. Instead of giving me a number, they said they would be right over.

In a few minutes there was a fire engine parked beside the Model Shop while I explained what we wanted to do to the fire chief. He suggested if we hinged the row of 8-foot plywood sections nearest the Model Shop so they could flip them up for access, that would work. That's how it was built. But just after they left, I was summoned to Harry's office.

"Did you call for that fire truck?" I explained my call to the fire chief. "Don't ever do that again," Harry yelled. "I thought something had happened." Harry was really upset. It is not good to upset your boss.

I learned from this experience, that it's a good idea to let management know what is going on before something happens.

Later during the test, the Ph.D. wanted to test the effects of crosswinds. The manager of the Test Engineers group sketched a quick design of a 4x4 foot wind tunnel with a large bellmouth, powered with high pressure air blowing from rows of small nozzles which would entrain and draw more air through the bellmouth and blow it across the praying mantis model. This little wind tunnel later grew into our Minitunnel research wind tunnel laboratory.

CHAPTER 6

The Shock Tube Caper

I needed to determine the frequency response of the transducer I was testing for an acoustic test at AEDC. These piezoelectric transducers have a very high frequency response. Their sensitivity is pretty level up to about 20% of their resonant frequency. I decided to measure the resonant frequency by applying an instantaneous pressure step using a shock tube.

Jack Headly, a jolly Englishman, and I used the Northrop 3-inch shock tube to apply a known shock wave to the transducer. Our shock tube consisted of a driver pipe eight feet long and eight inches in diameter, closed at the rear with a heavy flange and sealed at the other end by an aluminum diaphragm. This driver was pressurized to up to 3000 psi.

The shock tube itself was a heavy pipe three inches in diameter and thirty feet long. An aluminum diaphragm sealed the high-pressure air in the driver from the driven section of the shock tube where the instrumentation was installed.

The 3,000-psi air in the driver was abruptly released into the tube by rupturing the diaphragm. A pressure transducer at the open end would be hit with a shock wave of precise strength instantly jumping the pressure from atmospheric pressure (14.7 psi) to the pressure in the driver which will remain constant for a few milliseconds. This would bang the transducer and make it ring at its resonant frequency, which I then measured on an oscilloscope displaying the voltage output versus time.

Jack was tall and thin with a lovely accent, which I seemed to adopt after working with him for a while. We performed the tests on my transducer then operated the shock tube together for some other studies he was doing. We had "The fastest gun in the West."

Our shock tube used two diaphragms with a small space between them. We would slowly pressurize the driver to the test pressure, for example 1,000 psi. As the driver was being pressurized, the diaphragm interspace was also being pressurized, but it was shut off at 500 psi. The diaphragm thickness was sized to withstand 700 psi without breaking.

When all the instrumentation was set, we would open a valve to dump the pressure from the interspace rapidly. The first diaphragm would suddenly have 1000 psi across it and rupture applying the 1000 psi suddenly to the second diaphragm which would also rupture sending a pressure wave down the tube. By the time the shock wave had traveled ten tube diameters, about thirty inches, it was stabilized into a flat, uniform shock wave which applied an instantaneous pressure step to the transducer. Then it we had to unscrew eight large bolts, roll the driver back, replace the two diaphragms, clean out any aluminum flakes and bolt it back up for another shot. Different pressures could be tested using thicker or thinner aluminum or plastic diaphragms.

We were getting shots off about every ten minutes.

The shock tube could also be used to drive a shock tunnel. For this, a receiver tank with a little Mach 10 or 14 nozzle was bolted to the output end of the tube. The nozzle was sealed with Scotch tape so that the tank could be evacuated with a vacuum pump. Between the nozzle and the tank was a small test section with thick windows. A small model, usually a ball or cone shape was mounted in the test section. A 5-inch diameter Schlieren system was positioned to view and photograph the shock waves over the model through the windows. A Schlieren system is an optical system, which used flat and parabolic mirrors to make the shock waves visible.

To operate the shock tunnel, we would pump the air out of the sealed tube section and fill it to a low pressure with helium. That pressure was set using a radioactive vacuum gauge sealed off from the tube by a valve once the pressure was set. The receiver was evacuated with another vacuum pump, then the driver was pressurized to 3,000 psi. I would set the triggers on the oscilloscopes and watch the transducer response through Polaroid scope cameras. Jack would give me a count down, then BANG!

One time we forgot to close the valve to the radioactive vacuum gauge. I was watching the oscilloscope. Three, two, one BANG… rattle, rattle.

That shot sounded a little different, so I looked up to see a blizzard of papers, used Polaroid paper, and dust falling all around me. The insides of the radioactive vacuum gauge had been blown out of its housing, ricocheted off the floor, off the opposite wall, off the ceiling and crashed into the wastebasket by my feet. Luckily, no one was hurt. The radioactive sensor unit was still sealed and unbroken, so we set it on the table and began cleaning up the mess.

In a few minutes, two guys came into the test cell dressed in baggy white suits with white hoods, masks and respirators.

They swooshed us out into the control room and began running around with Geiger counters. Jack and I were clean, and no radioactive material had been released. The sensor used very little radioactive material anyway. Nothing serious, but it slowed down the fastest gun in the West for a while.

It was very hard to get the triggering right to catch a Schlieren picture of the Mach 10 flow in the test section. It only lasted a couple of milliseconds. Jack thought we could improve it using a larger driver section, so we got one made ten inches in diameter and ten feet long. For our first test shot with the new driver, we thought to use the shock tube,so we left the receiver separated a couple of feet down the track from the open end of the tube.

The large back doors of our test cell opened onto a tie down area of the Hawthorne Airport about ten feet away, so there were several airplanes just on the other side of the fence. We pressurized the driver, put on our ear muffs, and, just at the last second, Jack decided to close those big doors. He prefaced this action with those famous last words: "The pressure ratio is the same, so nothing should be different, but just in case…"

Three, two, one… BBLLAAAAMMM! A yellow flame shot eighteen inches out of the end of the tube and curled up over the open end to the receiver. This catapulted the receiver down the track into the door breaking a 4x6 stud inside the door and jamming the two doors together. Three ceiling panels (they were screwed on) fell down and all the dust that had gathered behind the walls and ceiling choked us out of the cell.

Jack looked at me and said, "Wow! Same pressure ratio, but a little more energy."

After much fussing, I finally managed to get one good Schlieren photo of flow over the model which I still prize.

CHAPTER 7

The Astrodata Data System

I first saw the Astrodata data system the day I was hired at Northrop. Tom Clouse was showing me around the facility and the wind tunnels. The main portion of this brand new data system was in the computer room directly behind the control room of the 7x10 Low Speed Wind Tunnel. The room was being remodeled, and the system was being installed.

The system was built to Northrop's specifications by Astrodata Corporation and sold through Moxon, Inc. When the salesmen first came to the wind tunnel, they flew into Hawthorne Airport in an antique Ford tri-motor airplane. After talking about the data system they proposed, the salesmen took Bob Lucas and Tom Clouse out to the old airplane which was parked at the Northrop hangar and introduced them to their pilot, Mr. Moxon, the company president.

The Astrodata was a digital electronic system which could scan and record 256 channels of force, pressure and temperature data from our three wind tunnels and record the data on digital tape for analysis by the computer system. It recorded data from three remote sites: the 7x10 wind tunnel, the Hypersonic wind tunnel, and the Inlet and Duct (I&D) test cells.

The heart of the system was eight six-foot high bays filled with transistorized slide-in cards of electronics with hundreds of little twinkling lights all over the front. It could have been a movie set for Star Trek. The lights twinkled continuously in a smooth pattern when everything was working right. When the lights stopped blinking, we were in trouble— no data system, no data, no testing. Everything stopped!

The twinkling lights were very reassuring.

For several years I never got very near to the Astrodata system. I was doing various R&D projects and another technician was the expert who maintained and operated the Astrodata. When he left Northrop, Luke made me a lead man along with Roy Eversz and gave us both the responsibility of maintaining the Astrodata system.

By this time the Astrodata had developed a reputation of being unreliable and hard to maintain. Many runs were lost with tape data unreadable, and the system was down for hours at a time delaying testing. Our problem was, how could we make the system more reliable?

When we started working on the system, it would intermittently stop working, and we would fuss around until it started again. Hank Laster was an electrical technician with gobs of experience and a great memory. He remembered the last time the system had a similar problem it was a bad card around this area in the rack. He changed a couple of cards, and the system would start working— for a while.

Roy and I started to suspect a problem in the Analog-to-Digital (A/D) converter, a separate rack module that put all the data into digital form for recording. We scheduled to stop testing on a Thursday night and pull out the A/D converter for repair.

Since Moxon Electronics was located not too far from Roy's home, he left early to carry the converter to them, and they agreed to work over the weekend to repair it. Roy came in a little late on Monday with the A/D converter under his arm, and we reinstalled it into the system. Inside the front door of the converter, we found a little transistor taped with a note: "Intermittent base lead." From that point on, the Astrodata started to become more reliable.

Another problem we encountered was many of the spare cards we had to repair the system were also bad. These cards had multiple circuits on them such as four Flip-flops or 13 AND gates.

If one of the circuits in the system died, we would replace it with a spare, but often, another circuit on the spare card didn't work which made some other part of the system to die. It was very frustrating. We had to find the bad diode or transistor on the card and replace it to fix the card, using the system itself to test if it was fixed.

Roy talked with Moxon and found they had a card tester which they ensured proper working of all the cards they manufactured or repaired. Roy promptly hauled all our spare cards to Moxon to check and repair. While he was there, Roy found Moxon had a spare card checker they would sell us. We hit Lucas with the idea and soon had a card checker of our own. Thereafter, every card we pulled out of the system was checked on the tester before being returned to the spares cabinet. We also inventoried our spares and purchased more of the different types of cards if we felt we needed more. Our repair times were getting shorter.

The next problem we tackled was intermittent connections between the cards and the sockets that they plugged into. There appeared to be something in the air corroding the printed circuit cards, especially the edge connector contacts. A common practice used to clean electronic connectors at many facilities was to rub off the corrosion with a "Pink Pearl" eraser. Roy and I had both been at the Arnold Engineering Development Center (AEDC), the huge Air Force wind tunnel and engine testing facility, where they used this technique. We both had tests where AEDC equipment was becoming intermittent and watched as the technicians "erased" the contacts.

These contacts, as received new from the factory, were copper plated with nickel then plated with gold. All the cards that were acting up at AEDC had been erased through the gold, through the nickel and into the copper which corroded quickly. We didn't want to make that same mistake, so Roy did some calling around. He had this wonderful ability to make two or three phone calls and locate the only person or company who can solve his problem.

In this case, Roy found a company created to solve the problem of corroded connectors. Eraser Corp. made fiberglass brushes designed to burnish off corrosion without removing the metal of the contacts. They really worked great and were inexpensive too. That took care of cleaning the connectors on the cards.

We were still concerned about corrosion on the connectors themselves mounted in the racks, thirteen to a rack, seven or eight to a bay, in five or six of the equipment bays. We contacted Amphenol Corp. who manufactured the connectors in the system. They told us the connectors were designed to be self-cleaning. They are polished clean each time a card is inserted into it. They recommended removing and inserting each card into its socket two or three times to clean the connectors.

These cards fit into the connectors quite tightly. We used a card puller to get the leverage to remove the cards, but our fingers got pretty sore when we tried to insert each of the two hundred or so cards three times. Roy got a little block of hardwood, rounded one edge to fit our hands and our "ge-innenk pusher" was invented. We would pop a card out with the card puller, then push it back in with the block of wood. Then out again and in again three times.

To do all this general maintenance on the Astrodata system, Roy and I started scheduling weekend work along with a couple of technicians. Many a Saturday was saved from a headache and slightly upset stomach by a hamburger and beer for lunch at the Red Barn just down the street at the end of Northrop Avenue.

We noticed some of the cards in the system were dirty and feared this dirt could cause some components to overheat and fail. We came up with a scheme to wash each card with pure 200-proof alcohol, immersing each card in the liquid and brushing it off with a paint brush. We would then blow each card off with plant air and place them in a warm oven to dry.

We did this by scheduling several days of maintenance down time between wind tunnel tests. With the help of several technicians, we removed each card from a rack keeping them in proper order, had their connectors burnished, and had each card washed and dried.

Meanwhile someone sprayed alcohol into each rack connector, brushing it with an acid brush. Then each card would be put back into the rack and inserted three times. We did this bay-by-bay until the entire system was cleaned. We scheduled this procedure once a year. Often there were several problems to fix after it was done. This procedure seemed to create some premature failures, which we believed would have failed at some other, less convenient time. Once the problems were located and resolved, the system was up and running and became very reliable.

As we were doing all this maintenance on the system, Roy and I found we had another problem. When the Astrodata system was installed, factory engineers made many modifications to make the system perform to our needs, but some of these changes and additions were not well documented. We followed a very systematic method to find and fix problems. From looking at the symptoms we would go to several cards that might produce those symptoms. When we found a card that was not working, we would check if all the signals that came into the card were fine. If one signal wasn't right, we would go to the last card that produced that signal and see if all its input signals were right.

We repeated this tracing of signals back until we found a card that had the proper signals coming in but wasn't working. We replaced that card and fixed the system. However, often as we traced the signals from card to card, we found we were off the road map. The drawings did not show the origin of the signal. Then we would holler over the PA system for Bob Gage, one of our lead technicians.

"Gage, front and center."

We would tell him, "3C10 pin 13, Find. Seek! Destroy!"

Bob would go behind Bay 3, to the third rack down and locate the wires in Pin 13 of the socket. He used hemostats to mark the wire as he pulled a little slack in it and saw where it came from through the wiring looms.

All the wires were white, so he would have to pull, feel and look to find the wire that moved when he pulled it. Bob would hang another hemostat on it and continue tracing until it terminated in another socket in another rack, often in another bay. As he traced the circuits, Roy and I would fill in the drawings with the missing circuits.

However, all too often, when Bob finished tracing the wire back to other end, he found himself holding the lose end of the wire in his hand. Then we had to guess where the wire had pulled out from to trace the circuit and get the system working. This didn't speed up our repair task!

The system had been wired using taper pins, a technique where a taper pin is crimped onto the end of the wire and the pin hammered into a hole in the socket using a tool similar to a center punch. The pin is tapered at one end, and the taper fits snuggly into the socket. Taper joints are very strong; we use them to hold the models in the tunnel, so Roy and I wondered why we were having this problem. The sockets were made by Amphenol Corp. but the extra pins we were using were marked AMP which we had assumed was an abbreviation for Amphenol.

WRONG!

There is an Amp Corporation too, and both make sockets and connectors. There is a several-degree difference in the taper angles used by the two corporations. The original factory wiring used the proper taper pins but many of the later modifications had used the wrong pins. The manufacturer suggested temperature cycling and wiggling the wires could have loosened the pins to come out. We had no idea how many bad connections we had in the system, but we knew the system would never be reliable or maintainable if the wires kept falling out. We discussed it together and with Bob Lucas. We felt the best thing would be to bite the bullet and carefully solder every taper pin to every socket.

This would be a major project— there were thousands of pins to solder— and the system would be down for several weeks to complete it. We blocked out four weeks of maintenance time on the wind tunnel schedule and lined up a couple of our best electrical technicians to do the job.

There were forty-six pins to be soldered in each socket and thirteen sockets in each rack. Each socket mounted very close to the other and hundreds of little white wires ran past where they were to solder. The light was poor and the back of the bays were cramped and crowded.

There were two things the technicians had to be careful of 1) leaving solder bridges between pins which would short out between the pins and 2) burning the insulation off the wires with the soldering iron as they reached past them to heat the pins and sockets. It was a miserable, delicate job, and they did it wonderfully.

What tremendous skill!

Sometimes when they got ready to solder a pin, it had fallen out of the socket and we had to figure out where it fell out from. After all the thousands of connections were soldered, we only found thirteen mistakes and errors. It took a while to get the system working again.

Unfortunately, one of the mistakes was a solder bridge between a power wire and ground which prevented turning the system on. There were hundreds of places where the power supply could be shorted out, so it took several days to isolate and fix the short.

After that, it was standard "chase down a missing signal and find the problem." We got the system up and working, having been into the valley of the shadow of death and come out triumphant. Roy and I doubted at times if we would ever get the system running again. We learned and even pioneered several maintenance techniques to keep the system reliable.

We had learned the Law of Spares: "Nothing will ever go bad if you have a spare for it."

I even learned to apply that to my truck. For about four years straight, each time I had driven my International pickup back to Pennsylvania, I had my water pump go out, usually somewhere around Tucumcari, New Mexico. Finally, I bought a spare and carried it with me. I never lost another water pump again, and the spare was still in the back when I got rid of the truck. The Law of Spares really works!

We learned the proper way to clean edge connectors of printed circuit boards. We learned the value of regular cleaning of the system and washing in alcohol.

A clean system is a good system.

We even regularly polished the front panels to keep it looking good. And we learned having good, faithful technicians to help you is worth its weight in gold.

CHAPTER 8

Testing the "Iron Maiden" at Ames

In 1970 the Air Force was looking to develop a new close air support airplane, the AX program. Northrop was proposing a modification to a light airplane built at home by our Chief Designer, Walt Fellers. The airplane was called "Sierra Sue" and had a pusher propeller in the "Y-shaped" tail. Sierra Sue was flown to Edwards Air Force Base and many Air Force officers liked how well she flew.

Somehow the AX program requirements grew until the airplane was nearly as large as a B-17 bomber. Northrop's proposal was the A-9A. The competition was the Fairchild A-10.

Figure 15: Northrop A9A

The A-9A was a twin engine, mid-wing jet with ten under-wing bomb pylons and a Gatling gun armament. We extensively tested a new idea for better handling when attacking ground targets— a "Side Force Controller."

One of my first off-site tests was a large A9A model tested at the NASA Ames research Center near San Jose, CA. The model was mounted on a force balance borrowed from Rockwell Corporation using a blade which entered the bottom of the model. It was used to measure the control surface and flap effectiveness.

The test was to be run in the Ames 10-foot pressure tunnel. It took a long time to pressurize and depressurize the tunnel for model changes so the control surfaces were remotely controlled using electric motors.

The inlets to the engines were faired over with large round frontal areas. This made the model resemble a woman with large breasts, hence the nickname "Iron Maiden."

41

Our Test Engineer was Fred Peitzman, who later became manager over the entire Aerosciences Lab.

In aircraft, when a servo system is used to control the aileron, elevator and rudder, a potentiometer is attached to the hydraulic actuator to provide an electrical feedback signal of the surface position. For a servo system to work best, the feedback pot is directly attached to the actuator rather than the control surface to eliminate "slop" in the bearings and linkages.

For wind tunnel models we want to know exactly where the surface is at, not the position of the actuator. As Instrumentation Engineers, our first task was to convince the model designer to have the feedback pot connected directly to the control surface. We had to build a controller to set all these control surface positions and then to calibrate the readouts. Due to friction, we would pound on the model with a roll of duct tape to simulate the vibration found in the tunnel.

When we got to Ames and started to install the model, we found a problem with the balance wiring. We were working under the tunnel where the old balance system was eight Toledo scales— "Honest Weight- No Springs." I was introduced to the tunnel crew and stood on a ladder to get the balance wires fixed. Later, I was interrupted and introduced to the second shift tunnel crew. Then I met the third shift crew. After I got the balance working right, I turned around to see familiar faces: the first shift was back.

They started running the tunnel test, and I got some foam rubber from the packing crates, laid down, and went to sleep to the roar of the tunnel. We were testing in the Ames 12-foot pressure tunnel which could be pressurized to five times atmospheric pressure or 75 psi. The control room was on the fifth floor, and the building had several windows that extended from the first floor to the fifth.

Mounted in these window frames were long glass manometer tubes filled with mercury to accurately measure the pressures. Of course, you might have to run up and down several flights of stairs to read the pressures. One day, one of the crew looked out from the fifth floor and saw two guys loading his motorcycle into a truck— I never saw anyone go down five flights of stairs that fast. They drove off, but the guy called security, and they were caught at the gate. The gates were manned by marines with rifles. The marines looked really sharp. The grass at Ames was well kept and green also.

There was a crane shaft the entire height of the building used to haul up equipment. When the tunnel was running, the Model mechanics and I had little to do. We amused ourselves by making little paper helicopters and dropping them down the shaft.

We soon found it was too much work to run down to get the helicopters, so I found an old resistor that was wound with lots of very fine, almost invisible wire. Passersby shook their heads as they saw grown men hand over hand pulling up an invisible string, like the TV comic who pretends to sew his fingers together.

Figure 16: The NASA Ames 12-foot pressure tunnel.

Our data was recorded by punched paper tape (computers were just coming into wide use) and later reduced and delivered to us during the day. We got to a part of the test where that system was just too slow. We needed to determine the best angle and position of the airplane's flaps, and we needed the data to set them to the next position. This was called "Flap gap and overhang" testing. That meant we had to reduce the necessary data by hand calculation. We had one adding machine available, one Frieden mechanical calculator, and one early model hand calculator. The data could be reduced using each machine for one part of the calculation.

Luckily, we had three engineers on the test— the Test Engineer, the Aerodynamist and me. Each of us would take the raw data from one data point (usually one angle of attack) and run it through the adding machine. Then he would move down to the Frieden and do the division required. Then he would finish the calculations on the hand calculator. As he moved out of one chair the next guy would take his place working on the next data point. Thus, we spent the nights playing musical chairs.

To add to our problems, the paper punch machine that recorded the data for computer analysis kept malfunctioning requiring us to repeat the runs. NASA had a technician whose job was maintaining the paper punch machines. We would call him, and he would bring over a replacement.

As soon as he left, the punch started giving bad data again. We called him again and he would replace it again with another, which he had adjusted and checked out.

Same thing after he left. We repeated this scene several times while getting no usable data. Finally, he brought over the master punch he used to set up the others, and we started getting good data. After getting off several runs with good data, he showed up and replaced the punch with one that he had just repaired. As soon as he left, we had bad data again.

Fred, our Test Engineer hit the ceiling. He called the NASA manager responsible for this wind tunnel, and he called the Air Force officer who was responsible the AX project development.

You NEVER replace a piece of working equipment with questionable equipment during a running wind tunnel test!

They brought the good punch back and left it there through the rest of the test. It worked perfectly.

When the test was over, "get-home-itis" set in. "There is a flight to LAX at 11 a.m. If we hurry, we can make it." The model came apart quickly and was secured into the model boxes as the mechanics worked feverishly to make the flight.

Unfortunately, the balance was stuck in the balance block.

This balance had been borrowed from Rockwell and was worth about $100,000. The balance is a piece of fine machinery and should slip in and out of the balance block easily. They pushed, pulled, twisted, and tapped on it to slip it out but still no luck.

The Model Designer, said to me, "Let us put it into a hydraulic press, and we can get it out and still make the plane."

I was responsible for the balance and I said, "No. Keep working on it. Pressing it out may damage it."

They took the time to do it right and got it apart safely, but we missed the early flight home.

For years after, this Designer and I disagreed over how much Molykote grease should be smeared on the balance before it is inserted into the balance block. We found using too much grease could get inside of the parts of the balance, picking up bits of dust and plaster which could interfere with the movement of the parts inside of the balance, fouling it and causing measurement errors. Able Corporation who built these balances later repaired one of our balances. Howard Ward, their balance designer asked me, "What are you doing putting all this junk inside the balance?" He explained the problem and recommended applying a light coat of grease carefully around the holes in the balance sleeve.

So, this Designer and I always argued whether to smear on a handful of grease on the balance or to carefully lightly coat it with grease. He was a great designer and designed many models for the B-2 Division, but we always had this disagreement when we were on a test together. **Good men can passionately disagree over techniques.**

CHAPTER 9

Supersonic and Hypersonic Tunnels or Hard Blowin'

I joined Northrop shortly after they built their supersonic and hypersonic wind tunnels. These were what are called "blow-down tunnels." Both were operated using 100,000 cubic feet of 3,000 psi air, stored in a bank of high-pressure bottles. This air was supplied to either tunnel through an elaborate system of valves and safety controls. The pressure in each tunnel was regulated by a servo-controlled ball valve to maintain the desired test conditions.

Figure 17: Control room for the Northrop supersonic and hypersonic wind tunnels

The hypersonic tunnel had a 30-inch diameter test section with a hydraulically run pitch system. The Mach Number is controlled by the cross-sectional area of the nozzle compared to the test section area. We had nozzles for Mach 6, 10 and 14.

To get the air to accelerate that fast requires a pressure ratio of 35 to 1650 which we attained using the 3,200-psi air upstream and a 100,000 cubic foot vacuum sphere downstream to dump the air into. Large pumps were used to compress the high-pressure air and pump out the sphere. Since high pressure air expanded into a vacuum will cool greatly, the high-pressure air had to be first heated to 3,200 degrees Fahrenheit to keep the air from liquefying.

At M=10, this tunnel could run for about two minutes before the pressure ratio dropped to 300, enough to unstart the tunnel. The supersonic tunnel had a test section two feet high and two feet wide. It used two-dimensional square nozzles to run at Mach 2 and 3.

The air in this tunnel was usually dumped into the atmosphere through a big smokestack, although it could be connected via a crossover pipe to the vacuum sphere for some tests. The larger nozzles used in the supersonic tunnel meant it used more air than the hypersonic tunnel. Therefore, the run times were typically about forty-five seconds.

Shortly after I joined Northrop, they had a transonic test section built to use in the 2x2 foot supersonic circuit. This huge test section weighed about fifteen tons, which

Figure 18: Northrop 2x2 foot wind tunnel showing test section window with model mounted in tunnel.

exceeded the capacity of out 10-ton overhead crane. Therefore, each time we had to install or remove the transonic test section, we arranged to do a load test on the crane. The crane had to be tested periodically to 150% of its rated capacity. Moving the transonic test section satisfied that requirement.

Transonic wind tunnels have walls with slots or holes to allow some air to pass through them into a plenum area around the test section. The shock waves in the transonic regime only sweep back from the model by a few degrees. In a wind tunnel, these shock waves reflected off the walls and hit the model, disrupting the airflow and screwing up the measurements.

When the right amount of air is sucked through the walls, the reflected shock waves are greatly reduced. This suction is adjusted by valves that open or close the exit area of the plenum and by the angle of the walls, which were also adjustable. Calibration data for the tunnel gave the best valve and wall settings for each Mach Number from 0.8 to 1.4.

Figure 19: YF-17 model mounted in the Northrop 2x2 foot transonic wind tunnel.

The model support systems were hydraulically operated to pitch the model rapidly through the full pitch range in the short run times of these, pausing shortly at each angle.

The test sections of all tunnels had quartz windows at least thirty inches in diameter and about five inches thick. This allowed us to use our excellent 30-inch schlieren system to visualize the shock waves produced by the models.

A schlieren system makes the density variations of the shock waves visible so they can be observed and photographed. Northrop's Nortronics optical group made the 30-inch front surface mirrors of our system from the optical windows used for star tracking in the Snark missile. The two 30-inch parabolic mirrors in our system had a focal length of about twenty-five feet. I don't know where they might have ended up now, but they would make a couple of great telescopes (pretty heavy, though).

A very bright light is focused into the first parabolic mirror to produce a 30-inch beam of parallel light, which passes through the test section, being distorted by density variations of the shock waves. The light is collected by the second 30-inch mirror, which focuses it onto the edge of a razor blade then picked up by a camera.

Light rays that are bent downward are blocked by the razor blade and produce

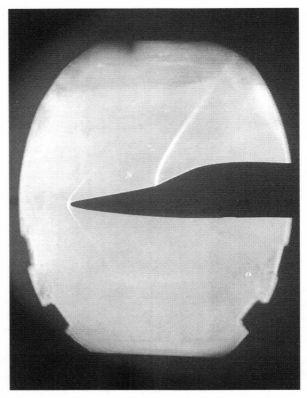

Figure 20: Schlieren of T-38 model at Mach 2. Note the shock waves at nose and canopy.

dark areas on the camera's picture. Rays deflected upward produce bright areas. This gives a sharp picture of the shock waves. The model appears in silhouette.

High-pressure air is very dangerous; therefore, the system of switches and controls used to supply the high-pressure air to the tunnels were designed to fail to a safe condition. Each valve had to be operated in the proper sequence or the relays that operated them would lock them out. Also, if a valve or power failed, every valve downstream closed to a safe position. A network of relays in the control room controlled all this.

Incidentally, I called our control room, "the Celotex blockhouse."

One of my early tasks was to modify this control system to make it safer. One time we were running a test in the hypersonic wind tunnel. I was watching while the operator, Charlie Nye, was pressurizing the system. He bled 3,000 psi air into the large manifold pipe which connected the four banks of high-pressure bottles to the tunnel. Charlie had just adjusted the controls of the serve controller, which controlled the pressure in the tunnel. As he closed the door to the controls, he noticed one of the meters flicker. He tapped the meter to be sure it was not sticking, and the ball valve

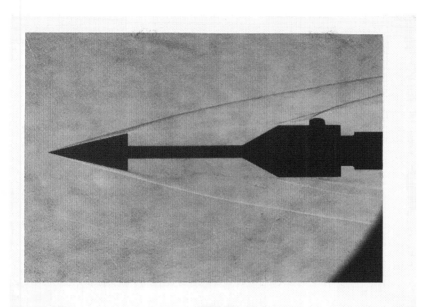

Figure 21: Schlieren of a model at Mach 10.

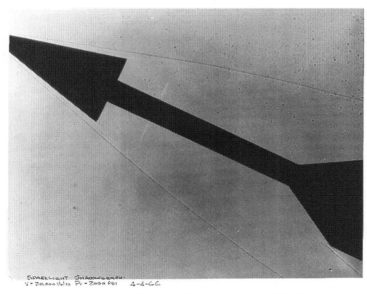

Figure 22: Spark shadowgraph of same model at Mach 10.

Note the thin image of the shock waves and
white expansion shock waves behind the conical section.

popped full open, letting the full 3,000 psi air instantly into the pebble-bed heater. The burst of air lifted all the little pebbles up and flipped the grate which held them. Charlie hit the "Emergency Shutdown" switch, which shut all the valves and opened the bleed air valve.

It was amazing how quickly eight grown men could squeeze out through the back door from the Celotex blockhouse.

Hot pebbles flew through the bleed valve, out the chimney and rained down all over the roof and parking lot,.

"What happened?" Charlie yelled.

We all ran outside to assess the damage. There was a layer of white pebble dust all over the area between the buildings and many little broken bits of hot pebbles melting their way into the asphalt. The paint on several cars was scarred and burnt but no serious damage, just a big mess.

The real mess was inside the heater and control valve. The heater had to be disassembled and refilled with new pebbles, and the globars, which electrically heated the pebbles, had to be replaced. I was assigned the job of finding out what had gone wrong with the valve servo-controller.

First, I tapped and banged all over the controller while it was still mounted in the console. I only got one flicker on the meter similar to what Charlie had seen.

Then I got the controller onto the table and started wiggling some of the wires around. The valve flew full open. I repeated that action several times, eventually locating a wire which had a bare spot in its insulation. This could touch the terminal which was the "summing junction" on the control card and apply 300 volts which told the valve to go to full open.

The controller had previously been sent to the manufacturer to be converted from vacuum tubes to solid state electronics. Someone there had accidentally burned the insulation off the wire while soldering wires to the connector while modifying it. It just happened to be in the most critical place possible.

The basic design of this controller was not fully "fail-safe." I suggested designing a new controller and was given the job of designing and overseeing its construction. I used commercially available solid-state, fail-safe switching circuits, which were doubly redundant. One of our electronic technicians built it and helped me check it out. That controller never caused any problems after that. We had a much more spectacular explosion instead.

Several years later, we were running a test for the Boeing company. They wanted to determine the amount of erosion from meteorite dust on a reentry vehicle.

We modified the tunnel to enable us to inject silicon-carbide grit into the hypersonic tunnel at Mach 10 and see the effects on some small test articles. The Mach 10 nozzle was made on Inconel, a very high temperature nickel-steel alloy. It necked the air down through an opening about three-quarters inch in diameter. The air was heated to 3,000 degrees Fahrenheit and the nozzle cooled by injecting cool 3,000 psi air just upstream of the nozzle.

We modified the tunnel to inject silicon-carbide grit— the stuff sandpaper is made of— into the air in this area. Then it would hit the model at the same speed as the Mach 10 air.

The test was running successfully for several days. We were even able to catch a schlieren picture showing the grit flying toward the model. It took a lot of photos using the spark light source to freeze the particles and get the timing right. Finally, we managed to catch a lone particle in the test section. We expected the grit density to be much larger, but the grit was few and far apart. The grit may have been thin at any instant, but we blew a lot of it into the tunnel, and it certainly did chew up the model.

Everything was going along fine, then---BLOOEY!

The tunnel blew up— sort of.

There was a loud BANG! The operator hit the "Emergency Shutdown" button, and one Boeing engineer came running into the Celotex blockhouse from the test area.

The rubber seal around the test section door, which usually sealed a vacuum in the tunnel, had blown out. There was dust everywhere. Hot pebbles from the heater were all over the floor, and we later found some had burned holes in the paper roll of a strip chart where they were caught and rolled up into the take-up roll. A lot of pebbles had blown out of the bleed valve and rained all over the parking lot again.

We found the grit had eroded the hole in the nozzle larger, which increased the air flow through it, which caused more heating of the nozzle, which started it to melt, which caused more flow, which caused to pebbles in the heater to float and go down the tunnel, which made the nozzle hole much larger, which sent more air through it, which sent more pebbles and pressurized the tunnel and caused the interlocks to shut down the run.

No one was hurt, but the tunnel had been badly damaged. Luckily, Northrop had insurance to cover the damage. We took the insurance money and ran. The Hypersonic tunnel never ran again. The circuit was later used for a calibration facility for mass flow measuring plugs used on inlet-airframe models.

The supersonic and transonic tunnels were used a lot. When a supersonic tunnel is started, a strong shock wave travels through the test section into the diffuser area where the air then "shocks down" to subsonic flow. That shock wave travels back upstream through the test section as the air is shut off.

Both the starting shock and the unstarting shocks can apply large forces to the model and the force balance. This is usually minimized by starting and stopping the run with the model at zero angle of attack.

Somebody realized in case of an emergency shutdown or interlock shutdown the model might be at a high angle of attack. I was asked to modify the interlock system to delay shutting off the air until the model could be returned to zero.

That meant power had to be supplied to the necessary valves and the controllers that controlled the model pitch system and air valve. I had an emergency generator installed so it had to be started before initiating a run. Other areas of the interlock system were changed also. This system performed well for years.

I also participated in the calibration of both the supersonic and transonic test sections. Wilford Wong was the engineer in charge of calibration the supersonic tunnel. Wilford had recently received his master's degree from USC and a little later was sponsored by the Air Force to attend the University of Tennessee Space Institute for his Ph. D. UTSI had just been built on the property of the Arnold Engineering Development Center in Tullahoma, TN, and they needed some students to work on advanced degrees. Wilford spent a couple of years there and recalled how he and one dentist were the only Orientals in the area. Wilford was later the engineer responsible with developing the inlet and duct systems for the YF-17, F/A-18 and B-2 aircraft.

There was never a nicer engineer to work with. Shortly before I retired, I told my second level manager our group should be ashamed for wanting to charge one of Wilford's projects four-hundred fifty man-hours to write a program to plot such basic data as rake pressures, which every other wind tunnel in the country did routinely. Wilford ended up plotting his data by hand. I was recording several pressures in the tunnel for Wilford during the calibration. He asked me to check the polarity of one transducer which seemed to be reading wrong. It was reading negative where it should have read positive.

Everything checked out ok, but it still read negative. Finally, we installed a longer pitot tube to measure the pressure in the center of the stilling chamber of the tunnel. Now it read as expected. It turned out the location where we had placed the old pitot tube was in the wake of an access hatch which produced the low-pressure region. I told Wilford, "What you sees is what you get." The instrumentation measured the pressures correctly.

After we got the transonic test section, it too had to be calibrated. This was a more complicated procedure as we had to determine the proper positions of all the movable valves built into the tunnel for each Mach number. These valves were moved and locked into position hydraulically. Since this tunnel was in the same building as the hypersonic tunnel with its heater, we used special synthetic high-temperature hydraulic oil. This required special seals. For a while every time we tried to set up the valve positions for a run, a flexible hose would blow off and spray everyone and everything nearby with hydraulic fluid. This green liquid liked to eat up shoes and polyester shirts.

We were measuring pressures with a 50-tube manometer which was about eight feet high and five feet wide. That manometer forever afterwards wore the outline of one of our technicians on the grid paper backing. We had a two-inch diameter tube with pressure taps every six inches along its length mounted in the center of the test section which ran its entire length from the stilling chamber to the diffuser. That left less than one foot between the calibration tube and the sidewalls.

I got the job of taking the Speed Graphic camera and taking pictures of the installation from the diffuser and the stilling chamber. It was a tight fit, but I was able to wiggle along the entire twelve feet of the probe taking pictures from all angles along the way. I was much thinner in my youth. When I finally crawled out, I discovered I had forgotten to remove the film slide. We never did get any pictures of that installation.

CHAPTER 10

The Heads-up Display or I learned Something from That

There were several times during my career at Northrop when things were slow and charge numbers few. During one such time, Bob Lucas sent me to the Dynamics Lab, the place where Warren Tribble worked. One engineer had been working there for several months developing the electronics to run a dot matrix screen as a Heads-Up Display (HUD) that could be mounted in an airplane in front of the windshield to display information but still be transparent to see through at the same time.

The display was a transparent panel about eight inches square made from a thin sheet of glass with 4,064 tiny holes in a 64x64 array. The holes were filled with neon gas, and the holey glass sheet was sandwiched between two solid sheets of glass which had sixty-four strips of thin gold deposited on their inside surfaces, running to the edge of the glass. The front had the gold lines running vertically while the back glass ran horizontally.

Thus, each hole had one vertical conductor in front and one horizontal conductor in back. If a large enough electrical voltage is applied to those two gold strips, the neon in that cell, and only that cell, would glow. The gold strips were thin enough you could easily see through the entire assembly. By selecting which dots were lit, a transparent message or picture could be displayed.

In order to develop the electronics needed to operate the display, the HUD was mounted onto a panel on a six-foot high electronics rack. No special electrical connectors were available to connect to the edges of the panel, so two 64-pin Amphenol connectors were modified to fit the panel.

An X-Y plotter was modified to scan a picture into the system which should be duplicated in the heads-up display. An X-Y plotter is designed to move a pen to a particular point on a piece of paper according to the X and Y values of a data point represented by a pair of electrical voltages. It had electrical potentiometers to measure the carriage position in the X and Y (or horizontal and vertical directions), and motor drives to move the carriage and pen to the exact position on the paper to where the pen was to write. The motors on this unit had been disengaged so the carriage could be moved manually from left to right.

Sixty-four small photo diodes were mounted to the vertical bar of the carriage so that they could be swept manually across a picture or writing on the paper and sense the light and dark areas to send their signals to the HUD display electronics. The potentiometer measured the position horizontally where the light and dark areas were vertically. In this way, the X-Y plotter copied the scanned picture on the plotter.

Neon lights, like each individual dot on the matrix board, take a higher voltage to turn them on to glow than is needed to sustain their glow. The voltage must be reduced further to turn the lights off.

A constant AC voltage, the "Sustaining Voltage" was applied between all horizontal and vertical lines on the display. No dots would light up if only this voltage was applied. But if a short pulse of higher voltage was applied to lines V21 and H11, the dot at location "vertical 21" and "horizontal 11" would light up and stay on until another pulse of negative or lesser voltage turned it off.

Thus, as the carriage was drawn across the X-Y plotter, the signals from the dark areas would cause the dots to light in the display corresponding to the dark areas on the picture on the plotter, creating a copy of the picture which would be displayed until another picture was scanned. Then all the dots in the light areas of the picture would be turned off by a negative pulse, and all the dark areas in the new picture would be turned on, resulting in the new picture being displayed.

At least that's how it was supposed to work!

When I got on the project, you could kind of make out the original picture on the display, but there were lots of dots turned on that shouldn't have been and lots of dots off that should have been on. The project engineer tried increasing or decreasing the sustaining voltage and scanning again. The picture would change, some dots would turn off and others on, but still the picture wasn't very good. Then he would increase or decrease the height or width of the turn-on pulse.

Same thing.

Then he changed the height and width of the turn-off pulses. Same thing. "Maybe if we changed the sustaining voltage with those different pulses." We were always looking for the "magic thread" that would make it work.

When the project was canceled and the time charge nearly used up, the engineer was assigned to another project. Trib and I were left with the display to use up the last of the charge member. I started checking if the right signals were arriving at the glass display connector. Many of the signals lacked the sustaining voltage or either the turn-on or turn-off pulses. We worked through the train of electronics for each one hundred and twenty-eight lines, one at a time.

Some lines had bad transistors in either the turn-on or turn-off circuits. Others had bad transistors in the sustaining voltage circuits. Quite a few lines did not make electrical contact with the gold strips on the screen. We also found several of the diode wires on the carriage had broken off from moving the carriage back and forth. About half of the one hundred and twenty-eight lines had some problem which had to be traced down and repaired line by line. The makeshift connectors connecting with the screen were especially unreliable.

After about a week the system was about 90% functional. Fixing one hundred and twenty-eight signal lines seemed overwhelming, but the repairs went quickly, and we made real progress. It could never have worked correctly with all those bad circuits. I learned that straight forward troubleshooting and a steady application of basic principles will solve a big problem step by step.

I certainly gained a real appreciation of the massive task of keeping hundreds of data channels working correctly or keeping all the complex equipment working on a large system such as a flight test airplane. I have never since been afraid to tackle a big job one step at time.

I recently helped a friend who is in aircraft ground school answer one hundred and fifty questions in planning a flight. He was overwhelmed, but he went through planning the flight step by step. The process is complex, but we worked through it and were able to answer all the questions.

CHAPTER 11

Cow Pasture Tests

Not all the tests we supported in the wind tunnel were run in wind tunnels. The Wind Tunnel Instrumentation group had the equipment and experience to measure forces and pressures in many testing scenarios.

One researcher repeatedly had contracts with the Navy to determine ways to limit bullet damage to fuel tanks so they could be made self-sealing. You may have heard the old sage about gunshot wounds, "Little hole going in, big hole going out." This really applied to liquid-filled structures like fuel tanks.

Firing a .50 caliber bullet into a 2-foot cubic tank filled with water would result in a ½ inch hole in the front aluminum panel and totally blowing out the rear aluminum panel. This man was developing computer programs to predict the amount and type of damage to create reinforcement structures to contain the damage. He came to our group for help with tests to verify their calculations were correct.

The back side of the container was being blown out by the tremendous pressures caused by the bullet impact. It was traveling through the water at such high speeds. He wanted us to measure those pressures so that he could confirm and refine his technique. During the span of my career, our group did several of these tests for him.

The first necessity for such a test was locating a place where we could fire and test a .50 caliber machine gun. Autonetics Corp. had a gunnery range in San Juan Capistrano, CA that had the proper permits and licenses for gun firing tests, and they agreed to rent it to us.

On our first visit there, they showed us their facility. It had a beautiful building, lots of testing equipment, and an enclosed gunnery range. The facility was very nice but unfortunately completely tied up with their own work. Then they showed us what we could rent: a cow pasture.

It was a large field which looked out toward the ocean. There was nothing in the field, no building, no power lines nearby, no water, just a hill to shoot at. We took it. Autonetics Corp. told us the cows were friendly but there was a mean bull we had to watch out for.

They didn't tell us about the bees.

These types of tests were always low budget. We investigated using rented semi-truck trailer, a storage shed, and even a garbage dumpster as a building to set up, operate, and store our equipment in during the test. We finally ended up with a small trailer set upon an area Autonetics had bulldozed level. Northrop paid to have several power poles installed to bring power to that location.

The pressures that we needed to measure occurred very suddenly after the bullet struck and faded out very quickly. Special quartz piezoelectric transducers manufactured by Kistler Corp. would have to be used to obtain accurate measurements of the dynamic pressures in the water.

This was my area of expertise. I ordered the pressure transducers, the cables, and the charge amplifiers we needed. Warren Tribble was the engineer who ran our Dynamics Lab. He was an expert in tape recorders and recording and analyzing dynamic data. His lab had special 14-track tape recorders which could capture dynamic data accurately. High frequency response was required from all the equipment because of the rapid changes in pressure that we were to record.

We would be firing into a metal container, a cube two feet on a side, which would be filled with two feet of water. The container consisted of a heavy welded steel frame to which square aluminum sheets were bolted. Each side was sealed with a gasket. The top was open.

Trib and I mounted each pressure transducer in a long piece of steel tubing. Each transducer was held into the tubing with two O-rings around their body which fit snuggly into the tubing. This was all cemented and water sealed using RTV silicone sealant.

This technique effectively provided shock isolation for the transducers. We were careful not to get any sealant on the diaphragm of the transducer as this might lower its frequency response and distort the measurements. Three of these probes were mounted on a separate frame and stuck into the top of the tank to a depth of six inches. They would record the pressures in the liquid at those locations.

The transducers were not mounted to the same frame as the tank because sound waves travel faster through metal than water. The shock of the bullet striking the metal plate would get to the transducers first and interfere with the measurements of the liquid pressures.

In addition to the pressure instrumentation, we had also mounted strain gages on the front and rear plates of the tank to measure their deformation. Two wire grids mounted on paper were installed just in front of the target to measure the bullet velocity by measuring the time when the bullet broke each wire and measuring the distance between the grid sheets.

This target was set up on the hill near the trailer, wires strung down to the trailer and hooked up. The machine gun set up and sighted in. The gun was loaded, and Trib would start the tape recorder and count down, "Three, two, one, FIRE!"

Bang!

Water splashed up as the tank was hit, then all the water dumped from the ruptured back plate. Two guys replaced the front and rear panels; someone would load another round of ammunition with a lighter or stronger charge of powder. Then we would do it all over again…and again…and again.

Trib did most of the testing for this test. He went to Capistrano for several weeks and got good data. The test was delayed several times when bees came around the test area and chased everyone away. Several people got stung, but they persevered and overcame the adverse conditions of cow pasture testing.

I was assigned to another test once we got everything going, but Trib and the guys did a great job. The researchers went away happy, scratching their heads and trying to understand the data.

Second Test

A couple of years later, they came back with another test. This time they wanted to get an idea of when the bullet dumped its energy as it passed through the liquid and how that might drive the pulse of pressure that causes the damage. An aeroengineer was involved also. His suggestion was to hang the target tank on a swing.

The tank would swing back in reaction to the bullet passing through, and its acceleration would be a measure of the force dumped into the liquid by the bullet.

$F=ma$ Force equals mass times acceleration.

The force could be determined at any instant by measuring how the tank accelerated hanging on the trapeze. The motion of the tank would be measured by high-speed photography. The goal this time was to fire up to three 20mm cannon shells at the target in a burst.

Aeroneutronic's facility was not available so we checked around and found that Northrop's Anaheim Division operated an explosive testing site near Riverside, CA. The guy who ran the place was an engineer named Carl Ramey.

The first thing I did was check whether or not Carl had ten fingers, figuring that anyone who played with bombs so much and still had all his fingers must be safe. I determined to always stand behind Carl whenever we fired. Carl was later laid off from the Anaheim Division and answered a job ad Bob Lucas placed in the paper looking for an Electronic Technician. When we found Carl had applied, he had the job request changed to "engineer," and we hired Carl. Northrop would have never hired a former employee in at a lower pay grade.

Carl and I went on several wind tunnel trips later, and he was responsible for getting me too close to a small airplane. I finally realized my life's desire and learned to fly. We rented a Piper Cherokee in Tullahoma, TN one day, and as Carl puts it, "I asked Bill to hold the controls while I took a picture, and he wouldn't give them back." But that's a story for another chapter.

Carl's test range was just off Freeway 60 in Riverside in the back of Stringfellow Canyon. Stringfellow Canyon was an industrial chemical dump, later to become the star player in the Superfund wars for cleanup of industrial waste. It was one of the most toxic places in the United States.

To get to the trailer and test area, we had to weave way out on a dirt road around open pits of red, green, blue and yellow goo; some had colored vapors rising above the surface of the liquid. You definitely did not want to drive off the road there.

It was costing us about two hours of drive time before we could start testing so I had an idea to save time. I arranged to have the company aircraft, a Piaggio P.166, fly the crew to Riverside and pick us up. I wanted those plane rides like crazy.

Flabob airport was a small field located very near the test site, so I arranged for the plane to fly into there. One of the guys helped load and clean the guns was an ex-submariner, and he was not happy about spending time more than ten feet off the ground.

Our test engineer drove every day in his Ford Shelby Cobra. That car was ALL engine! He told us when changing the battery, there was one point where he had to turn it upside down to get the battery in or out. He loved that car. Years later he took it on a tour of Europe. He said he was chased over the back roads of Poland by a band of bandits on horseback, but the Cobra easily outran them.

I couldn't make the first couple of flights due to other duties, but the Piaggio pilot swung around Mount Rubidoux and touched down on the narrow runway with our test crew aboard. He braked hard and still ran past the end of the runway and into the dirt. A very pale pilot told the crew as they left the plane, "I'm damned if I'll ever land here again. I'll pick you up at Riverside airport." Unfortunately, the air transportation only lasted a few trips. They canceled it as being too expensive, so we went back to driving.

Carl's trailer was located beside a large crater about two hundred feet in diameter and thirty feet deep. It had been bulldozed as a place to detonate explosives. Outside the trailer was a wooden platform with steps from which to observe the explosions. It was shielded by two 1-inch thick steel plates which had a 4-inch diameter hole and two 4-inch slits cut below it. Warren Tribble set up the tape recorder and instrumentation systems in the trailer.

The first few days we drove about fifty miles from Hawthorne to Riverside, me in the back seat of a Volkswagen bug. We knew the guys who handled the gun and loaded the ammunition were in front of us in a station wagon with a tripod-mounted .50 caliber machine gun pointed out the rear window. While we have all dreamed of taking a machine gun to the Los Angeles traffic, we determined to keep driving if we saw their station wagon pulled over by the cops.

The target tank was suspended north of the road from a large A-frame by a pair of chains. The guns, the .50 caliber and the 20mm M39 cannon, were positioned uphill south of the road. Anytime we drove by the road, we made sure the magazine of the machine gun was up and open before proceeding. In my opinion, it was not safe to go past the muzzle of a gun operated by guys who smoked while reloading their ammunition.

We got everything set up and fired a few shots with the .50 caliber. All went well. We built a timer which sequenced the start of the tape recorder, high-speed camera, oscilloscopes, and fired the gun. The 20mm cannon was fired electrically with a 300-volt pulse.

We got set up then for the first big test— the mighty 20 mm.

The photographer who operated the high-speed camera was named Ron. He set up to view the bullet pass through the tank and the tank motion on the swing. One side of the tank was heavy plexiglass so that we could see the bullet pass through the

Figure 23: 20mm M39 cannon similar to the one we test fired.

tank. We placed the transducers into the water from the top as before.

As we were getting set up, Carl told us that Ron had been here before. They were testing some shaped charges for the Anaheim Division. When a missile passes near its target, it explodes, but most of the explosive force goes away from the target. These guys thought to make four pie-shaped charges held in the round shape of the missile body by four explosive bolts. When the missile got near the target, the bolt furthest from the target would explode, all four charges would unfold like a chain, and all the charges would explode, directing their force toward the target.

Carl and Ron had done a test on these pie-shaped charges.

They used flash X-rays, and Ron's high-speed camera to measure the detonation. The engineer told Carl, "Don't worry. The backing plates on the explosive will just vaporize in the explosion."

Ron set his camera on a tripod looking through the 4-inch round hole in the steel plates. He was standing on the platform ready to watch the test through the camera when Carl suggested it might be a bit safer if he came into the trailer.

"Three. Two One. Fire." BLAM!

The camera came tumbling down from the platform. One of the tripod legs had been cut in two by the backing plate from the shaped charge, and the first four-inch slit had appeared in the steel plates.

"Just a fluke," said the engineer.

When they were ready to fire the next time, Ron was the first one off the platform. He had splinted the broken tripod leg with green tape (the wind tunnel equivalent of duct tape.)

"Three. Two One. Fire." BLAM!

Down came the camera and a second four-inch slit appeared perfectly aligned under the first slit. So much for armor plating! No machinist could have aligned those three holes more perfectly.

For our test, the tank was hung from the A-frame with two heavy chains and filled with water. The pressure transducers were placed downward at a depth of six inches in the water. Ron set up the high-speed camera to the left of the tank looking in through the thick plexiglass side. We would start the camera remotely with the sequencer.

The 20mm cannon, which was mounted on a large frame that had been designed for it, was bore sighted to the center of the front plate. The range was about one hundred feet. One round was loaded into the chamber by three mighty pulls on a rope system used to charge the gun. We were ready.

Almost everyone retreated toward the trailer, but a couple of guys wanted a closer look. One man was the closest and Carl recommended he move back. He did but only a few feet. When the gun fired, Andy heard something ricochet through the bushes about six feet in front of him. He moved back more rather quickly.

"Three. Two One. Fire." BLAAAAMMM!

A geyser of water sixty feet high shot up from the tank and obscured the target area. As the water subsided, we saw the tank spinning around. One chain had been broken, the transducers were dangling from their cables, which were twisted around the A-frame, and the camera had been knocked down. The tank frame was bent so much it would never hold water again.

WOW! What a shot!

We were all startled by the difference in force compared to the .50 caliber. It was useless to attempt a three-round burst as we had planned, so we packed up our stuff and went home to analyze the data.

Later Ron showed us the high-speed film. Remember, we were looking for when the tank swung back on the swing to determine when the energy was transferred from the bullet to the tank.

We saw the bullet hit the front panel and zip through the liquid in about ten frames, about three milliseconds. It passed about half way through the tank, then tumbled sideways before exiting the rear panel.

We expected the tank to swing sharply at about that point in time, but the tank didn't move.

The bullet left a trail of cavitation bubbles in its wake. This was caused by the water being vaporized by the bullet and showed clearly in the film. This cavitation tube then started to grow and grow until it filled the entire tank a few milliseconds later. When it hit the walls, it caused shock waves to bounce all through the tank.

Then the cavitation tube started to shrink back from the sides. It shrank and shrank until it was about the diameter of the bullet, just as it had been right after the bullet passed through. Shock waves again bounced through the tank, then the cavitation trail began to grow again until it filled the tank again. Shock waves went everywhere, then it began to shrink again.

The cavitation bubble continued to grow and shrink again and again for forty-five milliseconds, and the tank never moved a bit during that whole time. The bullet was now long gone.

Then the tank began to move... straight up.

Frame by frame the tank rose straight up, the cavitation bubble still pulsing and rattled by shock waves until it rose out of sight of the camera.

We all sat there with our mouths wide open. We had no idea what had happened. It had been very spectacular, but what phenomena were we observing? Also, the tank had never recoiled back from the impact of the bullet.

So much for F=ma.

Obviously, there was a lot of stuff going on in that liquid to rupture the back of the tank. Good luck in computer modeling that and reducing the damage.

Third Test

By the time we started the last series of gun-firing tests in which I was involved, Stringfellow Canyon was a Superfund Cleanup Area, Anaheim Division no longer maintained a testing facility there.

We found that Aerojet General owned a munitions factory and gunnery test range in Chino Hills, CA. They made 25mm Gatling gun ammunition and fired off a few randomly selected rounds from the production line to ensure quality control. They had the best facility we ever rented, and they had ex-military ordinance experts which were of great help on these tests.

There were several small blockhouses with electrical power, again located in another honest-to-goodness cow pasture.

"The cows won't bother you much but look out for the one-eyed bull— He's mean!"

Our assistant from the facility told us about the new guard they hired a few years ago. This guy was driving around from building to building on his rounds his first night. Just as he got to a watch-clock station on the main building, there was a huge explosion. Stunned, he woke up a few minutes later in the bushes alongside of the road. His little truck was in the bushes a short distance away, crushed like a postage stamp. The building he was checking was gone— just gone! He got up, dusted himself off, walked down the road, out the main gate, and was never seen again. He never even picked up his paycheck. Apparently, a ballast transformer in one of the fluorescent lights was dropping hot tar onto some ammunition stored in a storeroom and caused the explosion.

The computer model was well developed by this time, so we were testing to verity some of their mathematical test cases and testing some aircraft panels reinforced to reduce the bullet damage. We would be firing a 1-inch cube, the .50 caliber, and some 23mm Russian ammunition.

The 1-inch steel cube was encased in a plastic sabot that replaced the bullet in the cartridge. The sabot would hold together like the nosecone of a rocket while it was shot through the gun barrel, then the two halves would separate and fly off leaving the cube to fly to the target. Aerojet provided us with a good velocimeter to measure the projectile's speed just before impact. This would allow them to accurately match the test data to his computer model.

The Aerojet guys invited us to one of the other blockhouses while we were there to see the test firing of a couple dozen 25mm rounds for the Gatling gun. The Gatling gun was set up pointing into a cave just large enough for a man to crawl into. The cave had been dug by previous test firings. "When the tunnel gets most of the way through the hill, we'll throw some satchel explosives in there and blow it up. That way we won't be raining any rounds into Chino."

The gun mechanism was operated hydraulically, unlike the 20mm M39 gun we tested before which was operated by the gases that shot the projectile.

While they were explaining the gun to us and getting everything ready, I saw some cows walk through the area. One of them picked up the belt of ammunition they were going to fire in her mouth and walked off with it. There was a short delay in the test while the stolen ammo was recovered and finally loaded into the gun. We retreated into the blockhouse and the countdown began.

"Three. Two. One. FIRE!" BRAAAP!

In less than one second, all those rounds were fired, and smoke and dust poured out of the cave. What awesome firepower! What an awesome weapon! These weapons our military has should give the bad guys second thoughts before they start messin' with the good, 'ol U.S.A.!

I still have a couple of expended 25mm cartridges from that test in my room. When I moved to a new house in Corona, CA, I invited my next-door neighbor for dinner. No sooner had he come through the door when he ran over to my shelf, picked up my cow-pasture souvenir, turned it over and loudly proclaimed, "That's one of ours. Where did you get it?"

By coincidence, Tony was a plant manager for several Aerojet General facilities, including Chino Hills. Small world isn't it?

The researchers got good data to match their computer model using the water tank for a target. A new one had been built after the last 20mm test. Then we were going to test the 23mm ammunition, but the Aerojet boys stopped us. This was captured Russian ammunition. They wanted more information on the ammo before we fired it. First, they X-rayed it and found there was a loop of wire buried in the gunpowder. No one knew why so they contacted their friends in the military to find out more about this ammo. Their friends traced the history of the ammo.

It had been manufactured in Romania in 1959 and been captured by the Israelis in the Six-Day War and turned over to the U.S. military. U.S. ammunition usually has a brass ring around the bullet which chemically combines with lead and other materials to keep the gun barrel and rifling clean.

This ammunition had a brass wire coiled up in the gunpowder for the same purpose. The wire would vaporize and help clean the barrel for the next round. The Aerojet guys did yeoman duty helping us with this research. Many thanks, guys!

We finally fired the 23mm ammo into tanks where the exit panel was a typical fiberglass section of a fuel tank. We tested three types: an unreinforced panel, a panel reinforced with a fiberglass rib bonded to the inside, and a panel reinforced with the rib both bonded and sewn to the panel.

He unreinforced panel ripped open like the aluminum plate we had tested. Bad damage.

The bonded reinforced panel did a good job containing the damage. The cracks didn't propagate past the rib.

We had thought that the last panel would be the strongest but the thread that stitched the rib to the panel acted like a zipper and ripped the rib loose and the damage was much greater.

That's what testing is all about. Things don't always work the way you expect them to, especially with complicated things like airplanes.

The Day the X-15 Died

I was on another gun firing test for a different purpose. I screwed up the instrumentation on this test, and the Aerosciences Lab had to fix things up with our own funds. The research engineer wanted to measure the blast strength of the muzzle from a 20mm cannon. My friend, Wilford Wong, was the test engineer. Wilford later became the father of the advanced inlet-duct system for the YF-17 and the B-2 stealth bomber. Warren Tribble and another technician worked with us. We also had the support of an Air Force technician to load and maintain the cannon.

We used the same 20mm M39 cannon and test stand for it that we used on the other tests, but this time we tested at Edwards Air Force Base. All Air Force bases have an area where the guns on the planes can be sighted in and test fired. At Edwards, this was large mound of dirt east of the runway with a block wall in front with a pull-up door in the wall. We mounted the gun on the taxiway, aimed it toward the opening in the wall, and bolted it down.

When we noticed a rope hanging down from the door, we decided to sight the gun on the rope to hit it. We lifted the front of the gun stand with a forklift and backed the mounting screws off while Wilford put his eye to the bore sight and directed us.

"Up…Up…Up a little more." At this point, we backed the screw off the last thread, and the gun popped up suddenly ramming the sight eyepiece into Wilford's eye. He wore his shiner through the rest of the test.

Our tape recorder and other instrumentation was inside a van we borrowed from the flight test people. Power was supplied by a portable generator. Praise God, the van was air conditioned. Edwards can get very hot.

The goal was to measure the pressure and speed of the shock wave coming from the gun muzzle at different angles and distances. We had three pressure transducers mounted in probes as I described previously. This test preceded the other tests, and the probes were first designed for this application and later modified for use in liquids.

These pressure transducers were set at 10, 20, and 30 degrees off the gun axis a few feet from the muzzle. I also had half a dozen film gages to measure the shock speed by sensing a sharp temperature rise as the shock wave passed them (or so I thought). These were placed about six inches apart along the 30 degree line on the other side of the gun. While thin-film gages respond very rapidly to changes in temperature, apparently these were not fast enough, and we never got good data from them.

The 20 mm M39 cannon we were testing was like the old six-shooter, except this was a five-shooter, and the sides of the rotating cylinder were open to allow belted ammunition to feed in from the side. The round would be rotated one notch each time the gun fired. Once an ammunition round fired, it was ejected from the back of the gun.

Our Air Force sergeant loaded the gun by inserting a round in the loading chute and pulling hard on a rope with a handle three times. He pulled so hard both feet came off the ground against the gun stand. I don't think any of us engineer types were strong enough to do it. We were very glad for the sergeant's help.

We used a sequencer to start the tape recorder, trigger the oscilloscopes, and fire the gun. The gun was fired with a 300-volt pulse from a power supply. The first shot we fired didn't hit the rope, and the expended cartridge shot about the length of a football field behind the gun.

Our sergeant quickly decided he didn't want to go that far after each shot, so he set the ammo box about a hundred feet behind the gun. That stopped the brass, but we soon had an ammo box that was very dented.

It was almost as dangerous to stand behind that gun as in front of it.

Each day we would fly to Edwards on the company airplane. When I could, I grabbed the co-pilot's seat. The plane held seven passengers. We would take the van out to the test area and set up. At lunch, we disconnected the wires and drove back to the cafeteria, then back to continue testing.

One day as we drove near the Northrop hangar, we pulled over because a SR-71 was taxiing past us. It was led by a jeep with a .50 caliber machine gun mounted on it. Walking beside each wingtip was an Air Force sergeant carrying a .45 caliber M1911 Colt pistol at the ready. We figured they didn't want us to get too close to the awesome spy plane. The plane looked like it had been sculpted out of polished black rock.

As we flew into Edwards one time near the end of the test, it had rained the night before. We had to land on the main runway. Usually, we landed on the huge dirt runway where the space shuttle lands. The tower instructed us to land quickly as the base would soon close for the launch of the X-15 rocket plane.

We circled directly over the XB-70 bomber, which was at the edge of the taxiway testing her engines. The exhaust from those mighty engines dried off the lake bed for several hundred yards. The guys at the hangar told us to watch the B-52 take off with the X-15 under it, and before lunch, we would see it land on the dirt not far from where we were testing.

We watched the takeoff and saw the B-52 return after the launch, but we never saw the X-15. At lunch we learned the X-15 had crashed several miles away, killing Major Adams.

No wonder we missed the landing.

Later, Aviation Week magazine reported the X-15 had lost directional control and reentered the atmosphere sideways. She was carrying a probe which was moved in and out of the wing to measure the standoff distance of the shock wave. The probe's electrical drive motor arced badly in the vacuum of space and the electrical interference caused the directional gyroscopes to tumble.

Whenever someone tells you it costs thousands of dollars for a coffee pot on a C-5A, remember that coffee pot had to be extensively tested to perform safely in the pressure, temperature, and vibration environment of flight.

Those tests are expensive, but not as expensive as losing an airplane or its pilot.

Figure 24: The X-15 Delta1

The engineers analyzed the data from the test and were very unhappy. They spent their research budget on this test, and the data didn't look right. He told our bosses we needed to find out what was wrong, and our labs should pay for it!

Wilford Wong, Roy Eversz, and Warren Tribble tackled the solution to this problem. I later co-authored a paper with them which I presented to the Institute of Electrical and Electronic Engineers meeting in Ottawa, Canada. I thought it was the most significant paper I'd ever written, as it seemed many of the pressure measurements made in nuclear and other blast wave testing may have been in error, but nobody ever seemed to pick up on that possibility.

Wilford used the Northrop 3-inch shock tube to apply a known shock wave to the transducer probes that we had used in the Edwards test. Our shock tube consisted of a driver pipe 10-feet long and 10-inches in diameter, closed at the rear with a heavy flange and sealed at the other end by an aluminum diaphragm. This driver was pressurized to up to 3,000 psi.

The shock tube itself was a heavy pipe, 3-inch inside diameter and 30-feet long. An aluminum diaphragm sealed the upstream end and the other end could be open or sealed. The 3,000 psi air in the driver was abruptly released into the tube by rupturing the diaphragm. A pressure transducer at the open end would be hit with a shock wave of precise strength instantly jumping the pressure from atmospheric pressure 14.7 psi to 3,000 psi, which remained constant for a few milliseconds.

If the far end of the tube was closed, the entire pressure wave would be reflected back and the pressure doubled. A transducer flush mounted in the end flange would instantaneously see 6,000 psi. A transducer mounted in the side wall of the tube ten feet back from the end would first see 3,000 psi from the incident wave and a few milliseconds later see the reflected wave jump the pressure to 6,000 psi.

They had first calibrated the pressure transducers with standard techniques. What they found was the transducer itself acted a bit like the end flange and reflected the shock wave back. If the transducer diaphragm was of large enough diameter, all the shock wave would be reflected, and the transducer would sense twice the incident pressure (i.e. 6,000 instead of 3,000 psi). Smaller diameter transducers would reflect some of the shock wave and read a pressure somewhere between one and two times the incident pressure, depending on its diameter. The ¼-inch diameter of the Kistler transducers we used gave readings about 12% higher than the incident wave we had been attempting to measure.

I suspect similar transducer probes were used in many of the explosive blast tests conducted over the years, including nuclear tests. The transducers may have been of even larger diameter and been in even more error.

This solved the mystery of the bad pressure measurements we made at Edwards. This also made us very cautious of making dynamic pressure measurements of shock-type phenomena without dynamically calibrating the transducers in an environment like the test conditions.

CHAPTER 12

Helicopter Simulator

Northrop created several simulators to aid in the development of new aircraft. One simulator was the Large Amplitude Flight Simulator (LAFS). This was comprised of a cockpit mounted at the end of a 30-foot boom, which could swing up and down thirty feet and simulate +/- 5G's.

It included a 50x20 feet high geographical scene mounted on its side which could be "flown over" by a TV camera controlled by the simulator. This showed the simulator pilot a display as he "flew over" a lake, an airport, rivers, trees, etc. Someone pinned a large dragonfly to the middle of the lake to surprise the pilot with the discovery of a sea monster.

Another simulator used to simulate helicopters and VTOL aircraft was made from a F-5 cockpit mounted on hydraulic cylinders, which could cause the cockpit to pitch and roll a couple of feet to give the pilot a realistic ride. A very bright, point light source projected light onto a spherical screen 190 degrees side-to-side and 30 degrees up and down. This light was mounted directly above the pilot's head. Around the light source was a transparent plastic scene of an airport, about 3x3 feet with a control tower and water tower made of colored plastic pieces, which allowed light to pass through it to project a 3-dimensional view of the objects onto the screen.

This transparent scene was also mounted on hydraulic cylinders, which moved fore and aft, side to side, and up and down as the pilot flew to give a very realistic display representing the location of the helicopter around the airport. This display encompassed peripheral vision to make it seem very realistic. The light level on the screen was rather low so the room was painted black and the lights were turned off when flying.

When the pilot performed any maneuver, the cockpit would move to simulate the G-forces, and the display moved to make it appear the helicopter moved to where the pilot commanded. Then, very slowly, the cockpit moved to level and the display moved with it, so the pilot could not perceive that "fade-out" motion. This positioned the cockpit to respond to the next maneuver.

This simulator and others made later were designed by our Aerosciences Lab Design Group, built by our Model Shop with the electronic consoles and cables fabricated by the Instrumentation Group I worked for. When we got a contract from the army, Bill and I were assigned to operate and maintain the simulator for the contract.

The navy had several flight simulators installed at Pensacola, Florida. These were fixed-base simulators: the cockpits did not move, just the picture projected on the screen in front of the pilot. Even when using a simulator to train new pilots, an

Figure 25: Pilot flying the simulator.

Note the circular screen showing the helipad. At the top you can see the projector light reflecting off the plexiglass transparent model airport. This plexiglass box can move side-to-side and fore and aft to simulate the helicopters flight motion.

instructor is needed to teach the maneuvers.

The students learned quickly and had no problems using the simulators, but the instructors got airsick riding in the simulators with them. It was surmised experienced pilots expected to feel the maneuvers in the seat and got sick without that input.

The students didn't know any better, so they rarely got sick.

To prove this theory before the army bought any simulators, they came to Northrop to use our moving-base simulator to train several new helicopter pilots. Our first job was to test all these students for sensitivity to airsickness. To do this, we mounted a chair on a rotary table, which would spin it around like a top. The subject would sit in the chair blindfolded and be spun around until he didn't feel like he was moving. At this point in the test, we would quietly place eighteen wastebaskets in a circle to catch the vomit, whichever way the subject would stop.

Bill insisted the only time he got sick is whenever someone else threw up. The subject was told to tilt his head slowly to the left or right or from front to back. He would then feel a sensation of spinning off into space. This is the kind of disorientation pilots feel when flying in the clouds and do not trust their instruments. They are convinced they are turning and end up in a death spiral. They also get disoriented when turning to final approach on landing when they drop their lapboard and bend down to reach for it, taking their eyes off the runway. It is also a very nauseating feeling.

None of our future pilots got sick, and we, thankfully, did not have to clean up any mess. The army instructor flew the simulator to see if it "felt" right. He had over 10,000 hours in Hueys during Vietnam. The computer guys tweaked the constants in the flight equations until it felt right. One time we told him to flip the stick over and crash.

He screamed on the way down.

Then each student got to fly the simulator. When helicopter pilots are trained in actual helicopters, the instructor helps them with the controls for the first 10 to 20 hours. Our boys took off, crashed two or three times, then hovered and flew around after the first few minutes. Soon they were doing complex maneuvers under the instructor's directions. For fun, they would fly up against the window of the model control tower, then back away. They learned to make that helicopter do just what they wanted it to.

Bill and I took turns flying the simulator during lunch. When I first took off, the ground seemed to rush away under me with no connection between my control inputs and what was happening. It was a feeling like hitting your brakes in your car while skidding on ice—helpless. But in the simulator when I crashed, there was just a little bump. I'd push the 'reset' button and start again. After two or three attempts, I was flying.

The most difficult maneuver to me was to circle a bush a few feet above the ground and maintain a constant radius and constant speed while keeping the nose pointed at the bush. This required a lot of coordination, which I never acquired. About half-way around I just would whiz off somewhere.

I also crashed on purpose once. I screamed too. I totaled up eight hours of simulator time in this way. After a month the student pilots were very proficient at flying the simulator. For graduation, we rented a small helicopter, and everyone got to fly with the instructor. They each took off, flew around, landed off field, and returned without the instructor ever having to handle the controls.

Even Bill got a chance to fly a real helicopter, but woe to me, I was reassigned from the project before I got to fly. This test verified students and instructors could fly motion-based simulators without getting airsick.

Our students were sent back and phased into the standard Army training course and were nearly washed out. They could fly helicopters very well, but they knew nothing about safety checks, preflight, starting the engine and airport operations. But once they got started, they sure could fly.

CHAPTER 13

Flutter Testing or Now You See It, Now You Don't Models

The majority of wind tunnel testing when a new aircraft is being developed focuses measuring the forces and pressures acting on the aircraft. However, every airplane has a speed where the structure becomes unstable and starts to shake itself apart. This phenomenon is called flutter. We ensure this doesn't happen by testing special "flutter" or "aero-elastic" models in the wind tunnel.

The models are built to bend and vibrate just like the real airplane. This is done by making the wings, nacelles, tail, etc. with a steel frame that bends and twists under loads to represent the real airplane. Strain gages are applied to this frame to measure the amount of bending and twisting. The basic shape of the airplane is formed with pieces of balsa wood cut in segments to form the wings, fuselage, etc. The model thus looks like an airplane that has been sliced into a bunch of beef stakes held together as an airplane. This to keep the separate sections from rubbing together and interfering with the free bending of the frame.

The aerodynamic shape of the airplane is formed by the balsa segments so that it simulates the air loads of the real airplane. The little gaps between segments upset the smooth airflow so they are covered by cutting condoms into circular strips and stretching them over the wing and fuselage to cover the gaps. The rubber is very elastic and covers the gaps well without interfering with the flexing of the model.

Image 26: Flutter model in Northrop 7x10 wind tunnel.
Note the rubber strips over the gaps between sections of the wings.

Once when the Douglas Aircraft Company was coming with a flutter model, my boss told me to order a case of Trojans to support their test. A few days later I got a call from a lady purchasing agent, "What are you guys doing down there?"

I invited her to come over and see the test and gave her a tour of the tunnel. I think she thought better of us after that.

The model is held in the tunnel with a vertical rod but is free to move up and down on this rod. It is flown in the tunnel by the wind, and the elevator is remotely controlled to trim it to fly in the middle of the tunnel.

"Twang" wires are connected to the wings and fuselage by handles outside the tunnel and used to input a pulse manually to make the wings bounce or flap, and, if necessary, to clamp down the model to stop flutter if it occurs and save the model from shaking apart. Flutter can occur suddenly and parts fly off the model in the blink of an eye.

Strain gages are glued to the frame at various locations to measure the flexing of the wings and parts of the airplane. The strain gages are monitored on strip charts which show the deflections in real time.

Normally, when the model is "twanged," the wings flap up and down a few times, then the oscillations will damp out. This is shown on the strip chart as a damped oscillation that soon damps out. As the air speed increases, these oscillations take longer to dampen out. When the flutter speed is reached the oscillations continue. This is as fast as the airplane can fly. Often as the flutter air speed is approached, the onset of flutter may occur very quickly. The Douglas Aircraft company liked to use our 7x10 wind tunnel for flutter testing because we had low turbulence and could increase the air speed by ¼-knot at a time.

Even so, despite carefully approaching the flutter speed, the model would flutter apart before the flutter could be stopped with the twang wires. One instant the model would be bouncing around in the tunnel, and the next instant the nacelle or tail would be gone.

Then the test crew would grab the twang wires, yell, "Shut down!" over the intercom, and bells would ring as the tunnel did an emergency shut down. Everyone then went downstream in the tunnel to find the balsa wood and other pieces that had been blown down the tunnel. The breaking apart of a model told the engineers the maximum speed the airplane could be safely flown. If that was slower than the design speed, they would have to modify the airplane design.

The air speed in the wind tunnel was not the actual speed of the real airplane. The wind tunnel speed was scaled by the scale of the model. Thus, if we were testing a one-fifth scale model, the actual flutter speed for the real airplane would be five times that measured in the tunnel.

This scaling factor is called the Reynold's number.

When Douglas came to use our tunnel, they backed their flatbed truck into the rear of the wind tunnel building. Then we lifted all their packing crates to the second floor where the test section was located using the overhead crane.

The Douglas guys efficiently unpacked the model and began assembling the model in the tunnel. They always knew just what they were doing and worked quickly. The model would be ready to go by the end of the day.

In contrast, the Northrop flutter group were like the Keystone Cops. They built a F-20 flutter model that was painted red and blue. It was supported in the tunnel using 20-foot long torsion bars instead of springs. Torsion bars have a lower resonant frequency, which is why some cars use then for suspension. And like with an automobile, the engineers felt they needed shock absorbers on their system, so they made some using 5-gallon cans filled with motor oil. A wooden plunger with holes in it was connected to the torsion bars to provide resistance to rapid motion as it moved up and down through the oil. This resembled an old-fashioned butter churn. As soon as the air was turned on, the model porpoised up and down uncontrollably in the tunnel. Oil went flying everywhere!

The inside and outside of the tunnel were dripping. The strip charts were soaked. The intercom headsets were sticky for weeks. The crew had to go change clothes. It was difficult to walk around the tunnel without slipping. And everyone had to wash oil off the floor and the equipment. The tunnel was very slippery for weeks in spite of our clean up efforts.

They finally were able to get the model flying properly in the tunnels, but I can still visualize the model, quivering, pinned to the floor by the wind like a beached whale. We never had this kind of problem with the Douglas boys.

I was late leaving work one Friday afternoon when the phone rang. It was a man from Douglas who urgently wanted to rent the tunnel over the weekend for a flutter test. Unfortunately, everyone else had gone home, and there was no way to arrange for the test. They never called back, but I heard over the weekend a DC-9 had crashed. I hope it wasn't from a flutter problem!

Our second-level manager once hired a neighbor's kid. He first was assigned to the Design Group to file drawings. He couldn't handle that task, so he was sent to the Operations group and told to paint the inside of a large metal tank. He had to be rescued from the tank after he painted himself into the tank and got covered with silver paint as he crawled out. He then came to help me, and I asked him to drill a ½-inch hole in the wall of a wind tunnel. He soon showed up with a huge drill motor with a ½-inch drill bit.

"Where do you want it?" He asked.

I said, "I want it where the mark is, but shouldn't you drill a smaller pilot hole first?"

"I can hold it," he said. He couldn't. After walking the drill around the wall of the tunnel, he finally drilled a pilot hole.

He was then sent to our Dynamics Lab where he helped Ernie operating tape recorders. Ernie had been a technician in New York City and always wore a white shirt to work.

He asked Ernie, "Aren't you a technician just like me? Why do you always wear a white shirt like an engineer?"

Ernie replied, "I find I don't have to work as hard when I wear a white shirt."

The guy showed up for a week with a white shirt on.

One day when a Douglas Aircraft crew was setting up a flutter test, I got to the second floor just as Harvey, the Douglas Test Engineer, was hauling this guy out of the tunnel by the nape of his neck and the seat of his pants. He literally threw him out of the tunnel yelling, "Don't you ever come around here again!"

I asked Harvey what was going on. He said, "That guy worked at Douglas for a while. While we were preparing the flutter model, he walked into the model and bent the wing spar so badly it had to be replaced and re-strain gauged. Don't ever let him near me again, or I'll kill him!"

A few days later, he was talking with me bemoaning the fact he was being let go before his 90-day probationary period was up.

"I just can't do anything right! This is what happened when I worked at Rockwell. I didn't pass the probationary period. Same thing with Lockheed and Douglas. But I don't care. What I really want to do is be an airline pilot. I have been taking lessons in a Piper Tri-pacer, but I never have been able to make a landing. Every time I'm just about to land, the instructor takes the controls from me and makes the landing."

My worst nightmare is climbing onto a jet and hearing the pilot announce, "This is Captain _____. We will be cruising at…" If I ever hear his voice, I'm outta that plane!

CHAPTER 14

From Manometers to Scanivalves to Multiducers

Throughout my thirty year career in wind tunnel testing, we have been advancing in the ability to measure large numbers of pressures more accurately and less expensively. Looking back, I realize the advances in the state of the art have been tremendous Pressures are measured on wind tunnel models by drilling small holes, as small as 0.030 to 0.060 inches in diameter in the surface of the model at the precise location to be measured. The holes must be perpendicular to the surface and go through to an area inside of the model where steel tubing is soldered or epoxied to the back of the holes. The tubing is routed to a more open area inside the model where flexible plastic tubing can be connected to the manometer or pressure transducer.

The holes in the model must be small so they do not disturb the airflow. A typical model may have from a dozen pressure taps to over a thousand taps.

Manometers

When I first started at Northrop, large numbers of pressures were measured by manometer boards. Manometers measure pressure by balancing pressure with a column of liquid. Different liquids have different densities. Ten pounds per square foot (psf) is balanced by a column of 1.92 inches of water. One pound per square inch (psi) equals about 2.036 inches of mercury and 27.68 inches of water. A fluid called TBE (tri- bromo-ethylene) covers the range in between.

The manometer has as many as fifty or a hundred glass tubes mounted on a vertical sheet of plywood. It uses a small tank as a reservoir for a colored liquid like water. The reservoir is connected at the bottom of the board through a manifold which is connected to the glass tubes, each 100-inches tall.

The column of fluid in each glass tube is pushed down or up by the pressure or vacuum in each tube. The pressure of the air is balanced by the height of the column of liquid's weight. The height of the liquid relative to the reservoir level then is the measure of the pressure. Usually, a scale of inches or millimeters is attached beside the glass tube. You may have seen a mercury manometer in action on the wall of your doctor's office to measure blood pressure. You may also have seen a mercury barometer where the pressure of the atmosphere will raise a column of mercury about thirty inches.

Pressures in our 7x10 low speed wind tunnel were usually measured by banks of fifty glass tubes, 100-inches long, mounted on a on a vertical board. The pressures could be either positive or negative (vacuum) in our tunnel. All fifty tubes were connected to a manifold which was supplied with water from a reservoir. The height of the reservoir could be adjusted so that the level of water was about halfway up in the fifty glass tubes. This allowed us to measure both positive and negative pressures. We always had to be careful to not allow the water to go over the top of the tubes or it would get into the tubing leading to the model and give false readings. This was controlled by raising of lowering the reservoir.

The top of each glass tube of the manometer was connected to a small hole which was flush to the surface of the model using flexible tubing to measure the static air pressure

Figure 27: Recording pressure data the old-fashioned way using manometer boards.

of the air flowing over that location. Other tubes were connected to rakes, usually five or six small steel tubes mounted above each other at different heights above the surface.

A series of "pressure-taps" running from the leading edge to the trailing edge of a wing will show a distinctive pattern of pressures on the manometer board which instantly gives the Aerodynamist information about the air flow. The height of the liquid in each tube can be read manually or the entire board photographed, and the height of each tube measured by a machine which records the data digitally.

This procedure must be repeated for each data point in the test. One data point represents a particular model configuration and attitude. Thousands of data points are usually recorded during a typical test.

Manometers can be very accurate, but data reduction is slow and expensive. Manometer boards can also be quite messy when the janitor's elbow shatters a dozen tubes, causing glass and liquids to run all over the floor. Also, blowing the board over with too much pressure or suction gets liquid in all the flex lines from the model and is very difficult to clean out. The care and feeding of the manometers and their cameras were the responsibility of Dick, one of the nicest and most helpful guys in the wind tunnel. Those of us in the instrumentation group began looking at a relatively inexpensive way to measure all those pressures electronically and record the data digitally.

Scanivalves

Most pressure transducers cost about $500 each and were accurate to about 0.25%. Enough transducers for a hundred pressure model would cost $50,000. Too much!

However, a company named Scanivalve Corp. made pressure switches especially designed to switch forty-eight pressures into one transducer quickly, one at a time. Four, six, or eight of these switches could be mechanically ganged together to measure several hundred pressures with a handful of $500 pressure transducers.

Scanivalves required careful setup before use but proved very reliable during a test. Bennie, one of our technicians, was very good at delicate work. She became our Scanivalve expert, and I never knew of a problem with a Scanivalve Bennie set up. But before we could use them in our 7x10 wind tunnel, we had to prove they were as accurate as a manometer board.

We set up a test where we applied a known pressure to several tubes of a manometer board and that same pressure to several ports of a Scanivalve. We repeated the test with varying pressures, both positive and negative, and recorded the data with cameras and digitally. We found distortions from the camera lens produced appreciable errors using the manometers, but the Scanivalve data was consistent and accurate. We very quietly started using Scanivalves.

An additional advantage of using Scanivalves was we no longer had to run hundreds of flexible tubes from the model to measure the pressures. Now all the flex tubes terminated at the Scanivalve, which was on board the model and only a few flex tubes and electrical cables came off the model. This allowed us to measure large numbers of pressures while also measuring the aerodynamic forces acting on the model. Previously we had built two models, a pressure model and a force model, because all the flex tubes interfered with the force measurements.

To make all this technology work, Roy Eversz and I designed a Scanivalve controller to step the Scanivalves through their forty-eight ports and tell the data system to take each data point. It took a few milliseconds for the readings to settle from one pressure to the next, so we designed an adjustable time delay before recording the data.

Our delays were longer than most other facilities, usually a quarter to half second, because we waited until our four-digit display settled to within a few counts before taking a data point. Many other Scanivalve users scanned the pressures faster, tuning their system by observing the settling times on an oscilloscope, which is only 3% accurate.

Soon we were trying to stuff so much instrumentation into one model that our struggle became trying to put the top of the model on without pinching any pressure tubes.

The inside of the models looked like a big plate of spaghetti!

We had a new model of the F-20 built which was scheduled to be tested at the Calspan transonic tunnel in Buffalo, NY. We wanted to first check it out in our 7x10 tunnel and have some low-speed data for comparison. It was a force model with over two hundred pressures.

The schedule was very short, and we were installing the model piece by piece as it was being built. We worked overtime until we were ready to drop, came back, and worked as long as we could again. This introduced me to Northrop's chief designer's lecture on the difference between efficiency and effectiveness.

"Saving money by being efficient does the company no good if you lose a contract by not having the data you need in time."

The shop would finish an aileron with half a dozen pressures on it, and we would install it as soon as they brought it over to the tunnel. Meanwhile, two of my best technicians were trying to connect all the tubes to the Scanivalve in such a way the cover could be put on the model. They kept working routing and re-routing the tubes to put it all together, and they were getting a bit testy and frustrated.

I trusted their ability and tried to stay out of their way as much as possible. I could see their progress without asking. Rick was the test engineer, and he kept asking how they were coming along. One time I saw Rick was heading to the tunnel to see the progress. "Rick," I called. "Don't go in there."

"I want to see how much longer it will take."

"Don't go in there."

"I'm the Test Engineer. You're telling me I can't go into the test section?"

"Don't go in there, Rick. They'll kill you if you go in there and ask anything."

Rick didn't go in. After several days and nights of this, we finally got the model ready, and the test went ok and shipped off to Calspan on time— but just barely.

Multiducers

The next great advance in measuring many pressures in wind tunnel models and flight test aircraft was the development of multiducers. I have written elsewhere of my discussions with John Kicks, which may have inspired this development.

A multiducer is a group of thirty-six or forty-eight individual pressure transducers in a small package with the complete electronics to amplify and scan the signals from each one. Since each transducer was measuring only one pressure from the model, there was no delay to allow the pressures to settle out as was required upon switching one transducer to forty-eight pressures with a Scanivalve. The electronic scanning took a fraction of a second to record all the pressures from the multiducer. Reading forty-eight pressures with a Scanivalve might take nearly a minute. More data faster!

Two companies produced multiducer systems: PSI and Scanivalve. The PSI unit came out first. It had forty-eight pressure ports in a unit about 2-inches long and 1-inch wide and high.

One feature of all multiducers was a method of recording zeros and a calibration pressure. In the PSI unit, this was accomplished by moving a plate to the "Zero," "Operate," or "Calibrate" positions.

This plate had holes which first went straight through to connect each transducer to its individual model pressure port. This was the "Operate" position.

Applying pressure to one end of the plate would slide it to the "Zero" position. Here the front and back of each pressure transducer was connected to the common back or reference side of the transducers. That ensured there was no pressure applied to the transducer and its "Zero" electrical output could be recorded.

A transducer calibration was recorded by shuffling the plate the other way by applying a pressure to its other end. This had openings which slid in front of each individual transducer and connected them all to a common port to which a known calibrate pressure was applied. The PSI multiducer required about ninety pounds per square inch of pressure to slide the plate back and forth. This pressure was too high to use standard flexible tubing to connect it to the controller.

PSI used little metal coils, which we called "springy thingies" to hold the tubing more tightly on the multiducer tubulations. This system proved to work very well, but Bob Lucas, our boss, was skeptical the pressure was higher than the flex tubing was rated for. We opted for the Scanivalve multiducers instead. The Northrop B2 Division used the PSI system.

The Scanivalve multiducers used internal rubber seals as switches to switch to "Zero" or "Calibrate" from the "Operate" mode. This only required 30 psi to operate and no "springy thingies" were needed. One additional advantage of the Scanivalve multiducer system was they supplied a computer system to operate it which interfaced simply with the wind tunnel main computer. Most wind tunnels using PSI multiducers had to write their own software to operate them, a process requiring several hundred man-hours.

We had trouble with the reliability of the early Scanivalve electronics, but their customer service was outstanding. When we experienced problems, a quick call to Addison Pemberton, the president of Scanivalve, brought Addison up from San Diego in his T-6 airplane with spare parts and a technician to fix it. Once, Addison even flew to NASA Ames near San Jose for an emergency repair during a critical test. Later, Scanivalve replaced the old electronics with a standard personal computer programmed to operate the system. They gave us a special price for the new system on the provision we would return the old systems.

One of my first jobs when I returned to Northrop after living in Tennessee for five years was to integrate the new Scanivalve system into our data and computer system. They had budgeted four-hundred-fifty man-hours for this task, but the handshaking between the computers was so easy I solved in about one week.

At the same time my friend, Earl Reade who had transferred to the B-2 division, decided to return to our group. Earl had been working with me for about a week on this project when he got a phone call.

"I gotta go," he yelled and ran off.

A week later, he showed up with the following explanation, "I put in for this transfer and assumed everything was all set. That call was from someone telling me the FBI was looking for me. Something went wrong, and the paperwork wasn't approved, and I was AWOL. On these black-world projects, if you don't report to work for a few

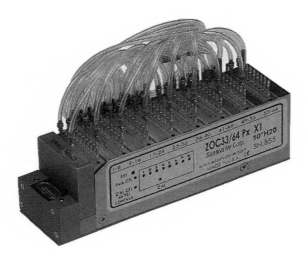

Figure 28: A Scanivalve "ZOC" pressure scanning module for measuring 64 pressures

days, the FBI looks for you to be sure the Russians didn't get you."

Earl was back to stay.

The ultimate test using multiducers was the F/A-18E/F Afterbody model. I was firmly convinced (and still am) the best way to measure the forces, especially drag, on the back end of a model blowing high pressure hot air out the nozzles is to measure a lot of pressures and integrate the results rather than use a "flow-through balance." The high temperatures and pressures always affect the balance accuracy.

This model would have over eight hundred fifty pressures and require twenty-seven 48-port PSI multiducers, which had to be stacked in two layers to fit them into the model. The high-pressure air was supplied to the model through two wing tip support struts and through the wings.

It takes a lot to plumb flex tubing from eight hundred fifty pressures to the multiducers and keep them from pinching or leaking during the test. Thankfully, the test at AEDC went quite well and gave excellent data.

That kind of test could have been done with a lot of manometer boards and cameras with many hours of reading the pressures from the film, but it would have cost a lot more and taken much longer to get the data.

It would have been impossible to get enough Scanivalve pressure steppers in the model and the lag times would have been too long to place the steppers outside the model and run long flex lines to them.

With the multiducers, the data was recorded in the fraction of a second and reduced data available instantly and displayed on line as we ran the test.

We've come a long way, baby!

CHAPTER 15

The Start of Multiducers

When we were working on the YF-17 program in the early 1970s, I adapted the use of very small pressure transducers called Kulites to measure rapidly changing pressures in the engine inlets of our wind tunnel models. I was known as the Kulite King of Northrop.

These transducers cost about $500 each, and I ordered them in batches of sixty. These were semiconductor transducers, made of silicon, and were only 0.070 inches in diameter. John Kicks, the vice president of Kulite Corporation, explained the semiconductor junctions for thirty-six transducers were diffused onto a 1-inch diameter piece of silicon. The 0.070-inch diaphragms were then punched out and fashioned into the small transducers.

John came to visit me once, and I took him for a tour of the wind tunnel facility. I took John to our 2x2 foot blow down tunnel and showed him how we had carefully managed to install forty 1/2-inch diameter CEC pressure transducers into the small sting that supports the model in the tunnel.

I told him it would be great if he could leave all thirty-six transducers on that 1-inch diameter slab of silicon, place tubes over each transducer for the pressures and run all the wires out the back. Then we would have thirty-six transducers in one package. It would be much smaller than our present sting package.

John was way ahead of me. He was not only thinking of measuring thirty-six pressures, but of amplifying the signals and electronically switching them to scan out all thirty-six pressure readings.

I also told John how we had calibrated the transducers as we used them for dynamic inlet pressure measurements. These semiconductor transducers are much more temperature sensitive than other types and must be calibrated frequently in the wind tunnel as the temperature changes rapidly.

For the YF-17 inlet tests we installed several solenoids and pressure regulators in my Craftsman toolbox. Thus, my toolbox became the first ZOC box (for " Zero, Operate, Calibrate").

About a year later a new company called PSI began marketing a pressure measuring system using small modules a couple inches long that could measure thirty-six or forty-eight pressures in a fraction of a second. The system could also be calibrated at any time during operation. I believe that PSI Corporation may have been started by several people from Kulite Corporation.

Around this time, I was at a seminar where J.C. Pemberton, who founded Scanivalve Corporation, was advertising his equipment. I told him the same thing I told

John Kicks earlier. The new PSI pressure measuring system was direct competition to the old classic mechanical pressure switching system J.C. had invented and Scanivalve Corporation sold.

After this I left Northrop for several years. When I returned, our department had purchased a new Scanivalve pressure scanning system, which worked like the PSI system. Scanivalve called the new system a ZOC system. I was beginning to think people were listening to me, but I wasn't making any money out of it.

Both PSI and Scanivalve systems had Zero, Operate, Calibrate built in. PSI went from one mode to another by sliding a plate back and forth using air pressure. This required ninety psi of air pressure to operate it. We felt this high pressure would give us difficulty keeping the pressure lines from blowing off in use. Scanivalve switched modes using rubber diaphragms, which required less pressure to operate which is why Northrop purchased that system.

When I returned to Northrop after five years, one of my jobs was to make this system operate with our data system. Several other wind tunnel facilities had chosen to write their own software to operate the PSI systems they had purchased but I found that the software and computer that Scanivalve used was easy to integrate into our system. We ultimately purchased three Scanivalve systems and used them successfully on many tests, but we did have some difficulty with the reliability of the electronics. Since these problems usually came up in the middle of critical wind tunnel tests, we developed a good relationship with Addison Pemberton, the new president of Scanivalve who developed the ZOC System.

As our Scanivalve systems grew older they became even more unreliable. Scanivalve came out with the new improved model, and eventually, we were able to replace the older systems. Addison was so delighted to have all the old systems finally out of operation that he held a special ceremony at the Scanivalve factory. He brought all the workers out into the parking lot, served them cake, and threw our last old system off the roof of their factory as a victory celebration.

Everyone cheered!

CHAPTER 16

The Kulite King

In 1972 Northrop began to develop the YF-17 in response to the Air Force's request for a Light Weight Fighter (LWF). NASA was just beginning to study leading edge extensions (LEX) to increase lift at high angles of attack when we arrived at NASA Ames to test our twin engine LWF configuration, which had highly refined LEX's. We ran at least half a dozen tests in the Northrop 7x10 low speed tunnel looking for the "Lost LEX," the super LEX configuration which we had run in early development tests but could never reproduce again.

Part of the process of developing a new aircraft is testing to ensure the air fed to the jet engines is fast and uniform enough for the engines to operate properly. This had always been done in wind tunnel models with pressure rakes located where the engine would be, measuring steady-state pressures. Then they would apply a safety factor to ensure fluctuations would not cause a compressor stall. That was how the project had been estimated and bid. Unfortunately, we found out we had to measure the pressures dynamically at each instant of time.

Engine manufacturers assume the air supplied to the engines through the inlet and duct system will be moving fast enough to be pushed through the first compressor fan smoothly. Each fan blade in the compressor is like a little wing, and like a wing, if it is not moving through the air fast enough, will stall. If all the blades stall, the engine may cut out and must be restarted. This can happen if every blade passes through an area of low pressure, even one time.

This makes fighter pilots very unhappy if it happens during a dogfight.

Our engine would make one revolution in about one 110th of a second. This meant we would have to measure pressure fluctuations up to at least 110 Hz for a full-scale aircraft or 550 Hz for our 1/5 scale model. To accurately sample the data, we decided to make our measurements out to 2750 Hz. This would require special instrumentation and would prove very expensive.

This requirement for dynamic pressure measurements came from problems General Dynamics had with the F-111 aircraft. Their inlet swallowed some turbulent, low-speed air, but Secretary of Defense, McNamara would not allow them to redesign the inlet. They had to fix what they had which forced them to operate very close to the stall margin for the engine.

The GE guys introduced us to Kulite transducers. These were very small pressure transducers about 0.070 inches in diameter made by diffusing semiconductor junctions onto tiny silicon diaphragms, like the way transistors are made.

Silicon being a form of glass, the diaphragms are glass welded to small glass tubes to reduce the effects of temperature changes. Wires were led out the back where a tiny tube was inserted, and the back of the transducer sealed off with epoxy.

These transducers were developed by Kulite Corporation in conjunction with John Kicks at Boeing Aircraft, Inc. Later when Boeing fell on hard times and so many people were laid off, someone put up a billboard that read, "WILL THE LAST ONE LEAVING SEATTLE PLEASE TURN OFF THE LIGHTS."

John moved to New Jersey at this time and became a vice president of Kulite. He proved many times to be our savior as we used these transducers. The first test General Dynamics ran using Kulites lasted only a few minutes. All the transducers were killed by little bits of dirt and debris flying around in the wind tunnel. Like glass windows, it didn't take much stuff flying at several hundred miles per hour to shatter the delicate glass diaphragms of the Kulites.

General Electric engineers showed me two types of probes used successfully to protect the Kulites. One type was a 0.070-inch diameter steel tube which led out to a steady-state pressure transducer but had a Kulite mounted on a 45 degree angle on a side close to the opening.

The other type of probe had the Kulite mounted into a steel tube which was held inside another slightly larger steel tube with spacers to keep the tubes concentric. A little protective cap slipped over the outer tube. It had a shield directly in front of the diaphragm of the transducer spaced 0.020 inches in front of it. There were three little slits along the edge of the shield which allowed the pressure to get to the transducer. The steady-state pressure could be read accurately by a transducer connected to the space between the inner and outer tubes. The slots and the close spacing of the shield allowed these probes to measure pressure fluctuations accurately as high as 5000 Hz. Wilford Wong and I selected this second type of probe for our applications. We were told we could get details of the probes from Dick Hoefflinger of North American Rockwell who had developed them for the B-1 bomber which would be tested at AEDC at about the same time as the YF-17.

Then I went to Arnold Engineering Center (AEDC) in Tullashoma, Tennessee for a pretest meeting for the tests planned for their 16-foot transonic tunnel, 16T. They looked at our YF-17 design with the inlets tucked under the leading-edge extensions and laughed. "Another Armpit Inlet," they called it.

They then proceeded to relate with some glee about the first F-111 test at 16T. When the tunnel got on conditions, they took their first data point and read 55% recovery, a very low reading. They shut down and rechecked the instrumentation and started the tunnel again. Another data point, same recovery. The AEDC test engineer then said, "That inlet looks like an armpit and it smells like one too. Shut her down!" And that ended the first F-111 inlet test (so they said).

We went back to Northrop with a lot of information and a lot to do. I contacted Dick Hoefflinger at Rockwell and arranged to meet and see what they had done. They were just a couple of miles down the street from us. Dick graciously showed me their probes, and we copied parts of the drawing showing their construction.

I took the information to our model designers, and they started making rakes for the Kulites. We would need forty Kulite probes, five per rake, eight rakes plus four spares. The rakes would mount every 45 degrees around the compressor can which was about 9-inches in diameter. We would only instrument the left inlet-duct because the right one would perform identically.

I ordered sixty Kulite transducers at $500 apiece for the test.

GE wanted the rakes rotated 10 degrees clockwise from vertical to avoid interference from a strut in the engine. This was what they had done for their engine tests. We asked, "Looking upstream or looking downstream?"

There was much discussion over this, and we sent drawings of our designs looking both ways and everyone thought we had gotten it right. But when they first saw our model at AEDC, they said that we had rotated the rakes in the wrong direction. It wasn't a major discrepancy though.

Kulites require a long lead time to make and deliver. We were on a tight schedule so a couple of weeks after I sent my order to Northrop's Procurement Department, I called the buyer to see when they would be coming. She told me my order was in her pile, and she would get to it as soon as she could. I explained these were long lead time items and even more time would be required to install and calibrate them. I also reminded her Northrop's Chief Designer, Walt Fellers, had personally guaranteed the Air Force we would make this test on schedule.

I got an icy, "OK," and she hung up. An hour later she called me back. "Mr. Anderson, your order has been placed with Kulite. Is there anything else I can do to help you?"

'Wow!' I thought.

For the next six months I couldn't do anything wrong. Each time I ordered anything I got a call the next day telling me my order was placed. Everyone who has dealt with the procurement office of a large corporation or government agency knows with the large piles of requirements they must comply with, procurement is very slow and independent. I guess they must have contacted Mr. Fellers' office. It sure worked well for me.

Finally, I had several Kulite rakes in my hand. Bennie, our expert in working with tiny instruments, did a great job gluing the Kulites into the rakes, soldering the lead wires, and sealing the rakes. About that point, Warren Tribble, who ran our Dynamics Lab, asked me, "How are we going to calibrate these things?"

I called Dick Hoefflinger, "How do you calibrate those things?" Then I putted out to Rockwell on my Suzuki 80 motorcycle to get copies of their calibration rig.

They made a small test chamber shaped like a little wind tunnel driven by a J.B. Lansing speaker in which the transducers in a rake could be calibrated against a standard calibrated microphone to determine its sensitivity and frequency response. They even loaned me the mandrel used to cast the inside shape of the calibrator.

I didn't know if it would work well, but I figured if we all made the same mistakes, no one would ever catch us. I drove back to Northrop with the little red mandrel in my

Figure 29: A typical "compressor can" consisting of 8 rakes holding 5 Kulite transducers each. The front of the engine compressor is represented by the plane of the front of the rakes at the top. The tubes carrying the wires and the steady-state and reference pressures exit to the bottom.

pocket and a drawing copy stuck under my coat.

Kulite transducers are quite sensitive to temperature variations. Both the steady-state zero point and the sensitivity (volts per psi) can vary several percent in a wind tunnel. The pressures we had to measure consist of a large steady-state pressure with smaller variations superimposed. To obtain the best accuracy, we would measure the steady-state pressures with the very accurate transducers provided at AEDC. We used an analog computer to add the variations in pressure from the Kulites and calculate the various parameters which General Electric used to determine the quality of the airflow to the engine.

Parameters such as ID (Index of Distortion), IDC (Index of Distortion, Circumferential), and IDR (Index of Distortion, Radial) were generated in real time up to 550 Hz. We recorded the peak values of these parameters, the time of its occurrence, and the instantaneous output of each Kulite.

One of the results of this test would be to have about fifty pressure maps of the worst conditions the engine might expect. GE would then reproduce those identical conditions using distortion screens and see how the engine liked them.

To calibrate the Kulites at tunnel temperatures (16T can get up to about 160 degrees Fahrenheit) a GE engineer suggested constructing a Zero-Operate-Calibrate (ZOC) box. Using pressure regulators and solenoids, the ZOC box allowed us to remotely apply zero pressure or a calibrate pressure to all the Kulites while the tunnel was running. The first ZOC box was built in my Sears Craftsman toolbox and installed in the plenum of the tunnel. It worked great.

My main duty during the test would be to adjust the ZERO knobs for all forty Kulites, run calibrations in the times between data points and constantly check that all Kulites were working properly.

This was very complicated model. We needed to test angles of attack from -10 to +50 degrees. The support system in 16T only goes +/- 10 degrees so we had to design a hydraulically operated mount for the model which would pitch an additional 40 degrees. This required a feedback resistor and control system which had to be calibrated also.

The tubing from forty steady-state pressures from the Kulite rakes and forty back side or reference side pressures from the Kulite transducers, tubes to measure a couple dozen other model pressures and forty 4-conductor shielded wires had to be routed around this auxiliary pitch mechanism and down the AEDC support system to the tunnel instrumentation systems. I always insisted we use Teflon insulated cables for our instrumentation because they would be rubbing against each other each time the model was moved. Sometime later, I was at AEDC talking to a Rockwell technician who was in the tunnel during a B-1 test. He was splicing and repairing a bunch of cables. When I said that Northrop always used Teflon cables, he said they were too expensive, and Rockwell wouldn't let them buy Teflon. They had to use the softer acrylic. Some people save a couple hundred bucks on cables and later spend $10,000 per hour of tunnel time repairing them!

In our model, the effect of the engine running was simulated by controlling the airflow down the duct using a hydraulically controlled mass flow plug to simulate various throttle settings. These plugs were matched with a flared skirt at the rear of the duct exit behind where the engine would have been on each side of the model. The plug position was calibrated against weight flow of the air flowing through the duct. Thus, we could set a certain weight flow to represent a desired throttle setting.

These plugs, as well as three other flow plugs used for bleed control for each inlet and flow through an Environmental Control System (ECS) duct, were controlled by servo systems in the control room. The inlets of modern supersonic jet aircraft are very complicated. The air which is approaching the inlet is supersonic and must be slowed down to subsonic flow by passing through a shock wave in front of the inlet. The quality and position of this shock wave is critical to getting smooth, uniform air flow through the duct to the engine.

Earlier aircraft such as the F-15, SR-71, and the Concorde, supersonic transport controlled the shock wave with movable ramps and doors in the inlets. These add weight and complexity to the plane.

Wilford Wong headed the development of a Mach 2 inlet which had virtually no moving parts. This system used a porous screen section of the ramp floor just in front of the inlet to stabilize the shock wave. The shock wave is controlled by adjusting the suction in several chambers under this screen to suck off the boundary layer air. This suction air was controlled by the bleed plugs on our model.

We took the model to AEDC for four weeks of pretest preparation and needed every minute of it. In the Model Installation Building, we installed the auxiliary pitch system into the support system in the 16T test section. The model was bolted to it and we started to install the compressor can with the Kulites.

There were large bundles of flexible tubing, stainless steel tubing, wires and hydraulic hoses to be routed through the model and down the sting. With the tubing and cables attached, the can would not fit into the model. John Black, the model designer, had the mechanics grind out areas of the stainless-steel model, and we tried again and again to fit it in. Grind some more and try again.

The technicians would say, "It's never going to make it that way. Let's re-plumb the can and route the tubes out from over here."

It would take a day to re-plumb, then we tried to fit it in again. Grind some more

Figure 30: F-18 model installed in the AEDC 16S supersonic wind tunnel.

The engineer is pointing at the instrumented inlet. Only the forward parts of the aircraft are modeled as rear portions cannot affect engine distortion. The white bundle of tubes over the engineer's shoulder and below the right side of the model were turned pink as described in the next chapter.

and try again. This went on for weeks, but slowly, we got the model together and ready to test on schedule. Finally, the test in the tunnel was finished, and we were ready to go into the tunnel. Changing test sections in 16T is an awesome operation.

First all the wires, tubing etc. for the last test had to be disconnected. The whole side of the tunnel, about one story high and 80-feet long made of steel several inches thick swings up to the ceiling to allow the test section to slide out.

It always reminds me of peeling open a submarine.

The test section is slid out onto the cart which is a large, motorized flat platform on wheels. The whole test section which weighs over a hundred tons slowly creeps, like

Figure 31: AEDC Propulsion Wind Tunnel (PWT) Complex

moving a two-story house, from the wind tunnel building to the Model Installation building where the test section in slid off into one of the build-up bays. Now the cart is free to take our test section over to the tunnel.

The process is reversed to take our model and test section into the tunnel. This is the time when everyone would lay pennies and quarters on the rails to have them flattened as the cart rolled over them. Everyone who has been on a test at AEDC has a collection of flattened coins somewhere.

I oversaw plugging all the transducer cables into the facility patch board and installation of my toolbox ZOC box in the plenum area of the tunnel. Everything must be tested and checked out. The control room was stuffed with extra equipment. There were racks of signal conditioners, amplifiers, servo controllers, oscilloscopes, and the GE Analog Distortion Analyzer (ADA). A special multiplexed FM tape recording system was in a separate room to record all our dynamic data.

There was so much stuff we couldn't see each other from out posts so the tunnel crew provided us with signal boxes. Before any data is taken, we each had to switch the light on our boxes from red to green.

The ADA, the heart of our test, was a tangle of patch cables and knobs, a computer as large as a desk and a six-foot electronic rack. This is where I spent most of my time switching modes on the ZOC box and twisting forty zeroing knobs.

Figure 32

Figure 33

Figures 34

Moving the 16-T test section from the Model Installation Building to the 16-T Wind Tunnel Building, where it will be moved across the floor and into the wind tunnel. The model, a F-18, assembled & mounted on the support system in the center of the test section & ready to run.

One oscilloscope was located at this station to display the "meatball," a display of the instantaneous IDC and IDR output signals from the ADA. The GE guys really liked to watch it, which resembled a loose ball of thread being bounced around by a cat.

Up to the time when we moved to the tunnel, I worked the day shift because that was when we had the most support from the facility people. These large wind tunnels use so much electricity they only run at night, off the periods of peak demand. The tunnel usually started running about 7:00 or 8:00 p.m., so now I started my shift at about 5:00 p.m. to be there during the final checkout and the first runs where I figured we would have the most problems. I stayed until we shut down around 8:00 a.m. Model changes were made during the day.

When we finally got everything ready and got the tunnel on-line, we found that we were flying in the clouds. The moist Tennessee air in the tunnel when it is first started condenses into a dense cloud which hides TV coverage of the model for two or three hours. This usually has little effect on the data, so we took a couple of data points. Recovery values were very low and most of the pressures in the core of the duct were reading low. Maybe we really had another "armpit inlet."

We shut down and checked all the rake instrumentation. Nothing plugged; nothing leaking. Looks good. "Let's run!" We came on line for the second run and had the same problem. Checked everything again. Same result. It was very puzzling.

When we came back on-line the next time, the model started flying in and out of the clouds. When the moisture dried up in the tunnel, the data started to look good.

It seemed water plugged the small space between the inner and outer tubes of the Kulite probes. This was the space that conducted pressure to the steady-state transducers and it plugged with moisture. That made the pressure readings wrong. When we applied a little suction to the probe to leak-check it, the moisture was sucked out, and it worked just fine. After the tunnel dried out, we had no more troubles from this. Tennessee weather can be very humid and confusing.

There are two conditions which limit the throttle range of the engine in an airplane. One involves too much airflow down the duct, the other, too little. If too much air flows down the duct of a supersonic inlet, it swallows the shock wave that should be in front of the inlet. This is called the supercritical limit and creates tremendous turbulence and distortion which stalls the engine. At the other end of the range, with too little flow, you get "duct buzz" where the duct acts like an organ pipe and sings at its resonant frequency. Our model duct buzzed at about 550 Hz, and you could hear it singing over the tunnel noise about a mile down the road.

Both conditions involved the inlet shock wave, so they only occurred when flying supersonically. Our test determined the mass flow limits for both conditions at various test conditions. However, this inlet would sing like a bird even at 0.8 Mach. This certainly confused Wilford Wong who kept walking around saying, "You can't have duct buzz subsonically."

To which I kept replying, "Wilford, duct buzz by any other name is still duct buzz." And "If it looks like duct buzz and smells like duct buzz…"

I think Will was getting a little annoyed with me. Later, he concluded the organ pipe-like buzzing was due to interactions between the bleed chambers and the duct. I spent the test running around madly zeroing, calibrating, and checking the Kulites. When I was ready, I punched my green button and the test engineer would take data. While the steady-state data was being taken, the dynamic data was being recorded on FM multiplex tape for later analysis by GE. This special tape system was one of the reasons we did all our inlet testing at AEDC. This system cost over $100,000, and AEDC was one of the few facilities which had a system with the special multiplex frequencies used by the engine manufacturers.

The basic FM tape recorder could record fourteen tracks of data on 1-inch wide magnetic tape with a frequency response from DC to 100 KHz. The multiplex system took each track and recorded nine channels on it, each on a separate frequency.

Thus, we could record about one-hundred eight channels of dynamic data on our forty Kulites, a few other Kulites, and all the distortion parameters from the Analog Distortion Analyzer.

A GE engineer once told me he had tried to explain how this worked to the French through a translator. The Frenchmen would nod their heads all through the explanation, then ask, "But where did other eight channels go?"

I could switch through the amplifiers for the Kulites and tell from their outputs if they were working ok or not. When one died, its output would get very spiky or noisy. Then we would disconnect its signal and replace its signal in the ADA with the Kulite nearest it or the average signal from the two or three nearest to it.

I had to get one of the AEDC technicians to turn the switch for me to check the Kulites because of the union rules. Sometimes this technician would be asleep and the whole test was waiting for him to punch on his green light until someone looked around the rack of amplifiers and holler at him, "Wake up!" Sometimes, I would let him sleep and check the Kulites myself. It was the only time in my career I ever had a union grievance filed against me. We all had a good laugh about it.

The first test configuration in the tunnel we ran was without the tunnel running. We connected a bunch of ducting to the back of the mass flow plug for the left inlet to apply suction to simulate the engine running just before take-off. This turned out to be our worst-case condition and resulted in a throttle limitation on take-off for the YF-17. Once there was forward motion, ram air cleaned up the flow, and the engine ran fine throughout the entire test range.

This test condition could have been discovered in time to modify the design if we had been able to test the inlet with Kulites in our Northrop Inlet and Duct Facility. This was my argument later to acquire the multiplex tape-recording system and Distortion Analyzer we eventually got at Northrop.

The YF-17 never had an engine stall during flight test while I heard the YF-16 had so many it was restricted to gliding range of the runway for a while, or so I was told. The rest of the test went smoothly, and we got tons of good data. We all went home very tired.

CHAPTER 17

The Great Mystery of the Pink Model

The YF-17 Inlet-Airframe model had four hydraulically-operated plug valves which were used to both control and measure the airflow through various parts of the model. These plugs controlled the flow through the left and right inlets and ducts simulating the flow through the engines. The plugs themselves were mounted on hydraulic actuators, and the position of the actuator measured to determine the airflow rate. There were smaller plug valves to control the bleed suction for the left (instrumented) duct and environmental control system whose inlet could affect the main duct airflow. Each of these plug valves were controlled by electronic servo controllers which moved the actuators and the plugs to the desired position for a required airflow. There was also a hydraulic servo system to operate the auxiliary pitch system which allowed the model to pitch to 60 degrees.

The hydraulic pressure to move the actuators was regulated by precision servo valves made by Moog Corporation. The AEDC facility provided the electronic servo controllers and Northrop built the plug valves and hydraulic system as part of the model. An AEDC employee, named Sam, was their expert on servo systems and helped us tune up the systems while we were still in the Model Installation Building.

We had a bundle of wires and tubing that ran external to the sting and were covered with white RTV sealant. We noticed after each run in 16T the white RTV was turning pink, a very greasy pink.

Everything was being coated with hydraulic oil.

It took a couple of runs and model changes to discover the pink juice was leaking from under the cover of a Moog valve, from where the control coil of the valve was located. We replaced the bad Moog valve and continued running. On the next model change, we found the new valve leaking in the same way. We changed it again, same thing. We had brought several spare Moog valves with us, but they were going fast.

Our designer, John Black, called Northrop and had Hank Karazewski send all Moog valves we had back home that would work. We inspected the bad valves and found a tiny tube was pulled a little from side to side by the control coils to allow hydraulic fluid to flow to one side or the other of the actuator was cracked. It looked like a fatigue crack. That was where the leak was. It must have been vibrating rapidly a lot to crack the tube.

We backed down on the gain on the servo amplifiers. That usually stopped any oscillations in a servo system, but it had no effect. We had no choice but to finish running the test in 16T using the spare Moog valves. By then the model was soaked with oil and the wind tunnel was so slippery we had to be careful not to fall. It had dumped many gallons of hydraulic oil into the tunnel. At least the tunnel would not rust anymore.

The model was removed from 16T to the Model Installation (MI) Building and from the transonic test section prior to putting in into the supersonic 16S test section. We placed the model on a table, got a hydraulic pump, and determined to find what was going on. We spent hours moving the valves back and forth with high gain and low gain. It worked perfectly. After a couple of days of futile effort, I got desperate. Thinking some shock waves in the tunnel could be causing something to happen, I started banging all over the model with a leather mallet. Tap. Tap. Bang!

The model mechanics were looking at me in that strange way again. Then I tapped the hydraulic line that led from the Moog Valve to the forward end of the left mass flow plug actuator. It was only about 4-inches long and had been carefully bent with a little stress curve before it connected to the actuator. When I it that line, the whole system began to buzz and hum. The oscilloscope monitoring the servo amplifier showed a strong 3 KHz. sine wave. Sam ran the amplifier gain up and down, no effect. Sam scratched his head. Now the buzzing wouldn't stop.

What was going on? I tried to dampen the oscillation by placing my hands on the model in different places. Finally, I moved the pressure and return lines a little, and the buzz stopped. The model was plumbed with ¼ inch stainless steel tubing for the hydraulics. Each Moog Valve had to be provided with lines to supply hydraulic pressure and return fluid to the pump. These common lines ran from Moog Valve to Moog Valve around the back of the model and had been tied together with safety wire to make them more rigid. When I twisted the two lines together, the oscillation started. When I twisted them the other way, it stopped.

Moog had told Karazewski the pilot tube that was failing inside the valves was resonant at 3 KHz. That little pilot in the valve had a high "gain." In other words, only a little movement of the valve produced a lot of hydraulic pressure change to the actuator. Any oscillating system must have three elements: gain, feedback, and a resonant element. Energy was being coupled from the pressure to the return lines for the feedback. Gain was provided by the Moog Valve pilot valve. Usually in servo systems, the gain is provided by the amplifier and thus can be controlled by the gain control. The line from the Moog Valve to the actuator was resonant at 3 KHz. as was the pilot valve.

What we had here was a little hydraulic oscillator that chewed up Moog Valves. The solution was simple. I had the lines between all the Moog Valves and the actuators made as short as possible to change their resonant frequency. And I had the pressure and return lines run some distance apart and secured with Adel clamps.

This was a very unusual case of simple physics.

We never blew another Moog Valve, and the test continued onto other kinds of troubles. Sam was the AEDC servo expert. He scratched his head and said, "I never saw anything like that before."

No, Sam, and you never will.

CHAPTER 18

Quick Shuffle Off to Buffalo

As we were finishing the F-18 force test at AEDC, we got word from Northrop they wanted one more test on that model before the proposal was due. The test was scheduled immediately at the Calspan wind tunnel in Buffalo, New York. As soon as the test at AEDC was over, everything was disconnected, and the test section was pulled from the tunnel and moved to the Model Installation Building. The Model Mechanics were disassembling the model even as it was being moved.

I had just been sent from Northrop in Hawthorne, California, with the calibration equipment for the balance. We pulled the balance as soon as the model was removed, and I took the balance and calibration equipment on the next plane for Buffalo. The model was packed in pieces and put into suitcases so that the crew could bring them as carry-on luggage shortly after I left. Charlie Nye had been sent to Tennessee to get the sting and bring it in a chartered airplane.

The plan was for me to get the balance to Calspan and have it calibrated immediately. By the time it was calibrated, the sting would have arrived, and we could mount the balance on it and measure the sting deflections under load. After this, the model would be there and all could be installed in the 8-foot transonic tunnel.

I arrived at Nashville airport carrying a heavy wooden box containing a block of steel and various parts used for calibration and another box containing a steel cylinder 2-inches in diameter and 14-inches long with a bundle of wires 70-feet long attached. This was in the days before the 9-11 terrorist attacks, and security was not as tight as it is now.

I explained what I had and why, and they let me on the U.S. Airways plane. Since both boxes were critical to the test, I couldn't risk checking either as baggage. I had to buy an extra seat for one of the boxes to carry with me. I had no problems at Nashville, but when I had to change planes in Pittsburgh, I ran into a policeman. He inspected my boxes and looked suspiciously at the balance, which, of course, looks exactly like a bomb. It took a lot of talking got get him to let me on the plane with that balance.

His last words to me were, "If that plane goes down, I'm coming looking for you."

I got to Buffalo, and we immediately set to calibrating the balance.

Meanwhile, Charlie Nye rented a Cessna 180 at the Tullahoma airport. The pilot was the technician who calibrated the balances at AEDC. He went AWOL from the wind tunnel for a couple of days, and he and Charlie tied the sting into the Cessna with the end of it reaching well into the tail of the airplane and took off for Buffalo. Charlie later told me they had dodged storms and bounced in turbulence all the way, but he got the sting there when we needed it. We measured the sting deflections and mounted the sting and balance in the tunnel in preparation for the arrival of the model.

Meanwhile, back at Nashville the rest of the crew had packed the model parts in several suitcases and wooden boxes with handles, each man carrying one to the plane. They all got on and sat down when Stan Ton realized he had forgotten his box. He had left it at the gate. He jumped up and ran back to the gate. He was gone a few minutes, and the flight crew closed the door, and the plane started to taxi out to the runway. Everybody kept looking around. "Where was Stan?" The plane got half-way to the runway when it stopped, and the pilot announced, "We've forgotten something back at the gate and we're going back for it." Stairs were rolled up to the plane and in walks Stan, box in hand. As he walked down the aisle, everyone on the plane applauded him. We got ALL the model there in time.

After the model was installed and running, we sent the extra crew-members home. Only Fred Peitzman, Charlie Nye, Stan Ton, and I stayed for the whole test. Stan was the only model builder there. Charlie was the designer, and Fred was the test engineer. Whenever we had a model change, it became a race between two engineers, Fred and me, against Stan. Fred and I would take the left wing, and Stan the right one. Fred would remove the screws from the leaning edge flap, replace the brackets with brackets made for the new angle, and I would do the same on the trailing edge flap. We would be tightening our screws while Stan would have both flaps changed and was mixing dental plaster to fill the holes. If we were going really fast Fred and I might get started plastering the holes before Stan came over to finish our side. Stan always won against both of us.

Charlie was building a house near Lake Tahoe at that time. It was of post and beam construction, all wood, like the way barns used to be built. On our first day off, Charlie wanted to visit antique shops, looking for tools and fixtures for his house. I went with him. We drove the back roads through New York and down into Pennsylvania, stopping at shops along the way. At a little general store in Pennsylvania, a man told us about a guy with antiques "out along that road there," pointing to the cross road where the store was located.

We drove down the road a couple of miles and saw a big barn with the word, "ANTIQUES" painted in the side. My Gosh!! What a place!

Old stuff was piled everywhere. He had EVERYTHING! We nosed around for a couple of hours, and Charlie found just what he had been looking for, an old hand-operated drill press for drilling ship's beams so they can be pinned together with large wooden pins. That drill press went home in the model shipping boxes, along with a couple of bicycles. It was common to buy something while on a trip and ship it home in the model box. One time two guys bought Martin guitars from the factory in Tennessee and sent them home. I have shipped back country hams and Falls Mill Flour from there. I guess the test was successful because we soon had a contract and were building the fuselage for the F-18 and wind tunnel testing to refine the aircraft.

CHAPTER 19

McDonnell's Madison Avenue Test Engineer

McDonnell-Douglas engineers informed us at Northrop they had solved all the inlet-duct problems with testing in their 4-foot blow-down tunnel in St. Louis, MO. The test engineer and several others went with me back to St. Louis to see their wind tunnels, and their new Analog Distortion Analyzer (ADA). Tom, the test engineer was tall and always knocking chips from the tops of doorways at Northrop. He managed to hit his head on the low-speed wind tunnel during the tour. The manager of their instrumentation group reminded me somewhat of Bob Lucas. His group was building a new Analog Distortion Analyzer or ADA for the test. The other ADA they designed and built was created to calculate the distortion parameters used by Pratt and Whitney Engine Company. The F-18 would use two GE F-101 engines, so the new ADA was deigned to calculate GE distortion parameters.

Later, the Society of Automotive Engineers (SAE) would adopt a standard for aircraft engine distortion parameters which were similar to the GE parameters but modified slightly. For a while, I believe I was the only guy at Northrop who understood both parameters because the P&W methodology was like RMS AC voltage calculations used in electrical engineering.

The ADA itself was a six-foot tall, two-bay electrical rack mounted on large casters. The right-hand bay contained several digital panel meters used to display the maximum values of the various parameters during the run. This machine would be placed in the control room and be the center piece for the test. It was well designed with many checks and cross-checks to ensure the data was valid. It was later delivered to AEDC hanging out of the back of a station wagon covered with plastic. It was, of course, raining at the time.

We first met our tall handsome Madison Avenue Test Engineer (MATE), whose name gratefully escapes me now, at the AEDC pretest meeting. Since the inlet problems were all resolved by McDonnell-Douglas, they said, they only planned for three or four runs in the 16-foot transonic tunnel and a couple of runs in the 16-foot supersonic tunnel, just to verify the inlet performance. When AEDC engineers asked what the contingency plan was, MATE replied, "There is no contingency plan. We will test the long fence first, then the short one. This will work."

We all looked at each other. This sounded ominous to us.

The model looked pretty much like the YF-17 Inlet-Airframe model except the scale was changed from 0.20 to 0.189. This let the larger airplane use the same compressor can with all the Kulite transducers and rakes which were used in the YF-17 model. The added pitch mechanism was also modified to allow the model to pitch

Figure 35: GE Analog Distortion Analyzer.

to a 60 degree angle of attack.

While we were assembling the model in the Model Installation building, two days before the test, MATE asked the model designer, John Black if we could remove a quarter inch from the nose all around. The nose, like the rest of the model, was made of stainless steel. It was almost 3-feet long. John chased him out of the building with a steel pipe. That was one change request we didn't make.

The Navy wanted to test this model at NASA Ames Research Center, but I made the point that facility did not have the tape-recording equipment or experience in this type of testing that AEDC had. It would cost $200,000-300,000 more to go to Ames. Management backed me up and the Navy finally agreed to AEDC. The F-18 model had the same hydraulically operated plug valves and pitch system as the YF-17 and so required a small rack of servo controllers from AEDC. They were ready for us. This rack was labeled in large letters:

ANOTHER
NAVY
USAF
ARO
AEDC
MCDONNELL-DOUGLAS
NORTHROP
WIND TUNNEL TEST

They also supplied us with an intercom system to aid us in checking out the instrumentation: two tin cans and a length of string labeled, "Northrop Intercom."

We leak-checked our systems in the MI building using little vacuum boxes which had been built by one of our technicians. This box produced a vacuum by using the venturi effect from plant air flowing through it and out a little "smokestack" of ¼-inch tubing. The length of this smokestack was critical to create the greatest vacuum. The air was turned on by pushing a little button valve, and the vacuum was measured on a Kollsman vacuum gauge.

One of the guys and I found the "smokestack" made a great catapult for Q-tips. Drop a Q-tip in the stack, push the button, and the Q-tip launched like a little rocket. The model build-up area of the MI building had high ceilings and soon it was decorated with numerous Q-tips which were painted with various colored stripes.

Benny was our best delicate wiring technician, and for some reason (probably greater maturity), our antics with the Q-tips annoyed her greatly. "Why don't you children grow up?"

Those Q-tips remained embedded in the ceiling of the MI building for over ten years, but the last time I was there in 1997, they were gone. The ceiling had been redone.

We moved the model and test section to the tunnel and got everything installed and checked out. The tunnel only ran at night, from 8 p.m. to 8 a.m. Preflight checkout started around 5 PM so when we were ready, I switched myself to the 5 p.m. to 8 a.m. shift. With the usual start-up problems, we got the tunnel on line around 11 PM. We took a couple of data points and something was wrong. Recovery was 58% and the distortion numbers were very high. We shut down the tunnel and rechecked all the instrumentation. It looked ok. We came on line again and took more data.

The data was good, the inlet was not.

While the tunnel churned away at $10,000 per hour, Madison Avenue was on the phone talking to people at St. Louis at 2 a.m.! The impossible happened, and we had no contingency plan.

At one point during this fiasco, someone at St. Louis didn't believe a splitter plate was needed to keep the inlet from ingesting low energy boundary-layer air. He had John Black make a wooden fairing from the nose to the edge of the ramp. When we tested this configuration, we had distortion numbers over 60%— a record for distortion I think still stands!

We pulled out of that test early and went back to redesign the model to solve the distortion problems.

CHAPTER 20

Which Motel This Time?

One of our former secretaries got a promotion to the Northrop corporate offices and she related a story from her new boss: This man was with another man supporting a classified test in Alamogordo, NM, for a couple of weeks. One security requirement was they must change hotels every day. Supposedly, this was to confuse any spies and keep from drawing attention to themselves. However, there were only two hotels in Alamogordo, right across the street from each other. After three days, locals started lining the street to watch this ritual of two guys checking out of one hotel, carrying their suitcases across the street and checking into the other hotel. Black-world security sometimes made little sense.

Our Inlet and Duct Test facility had a roll-up door, which could be opened with a chain lift. It also had an electric motor to open it with a push button. When we were testing something from the black world there, security required the chain be locked with a special padlock so it could not be used to open the door. However, the door could still be opened with the motor by pushing the "open" button. We showed them anyone could still open the door, but they didn't care. They had followed their procedures. Go figure!

I noticed on some trips to AEDC that some test engineers had us stay at Holiday Inn, our usual hotel, but others had us stay in the Quality Inn. What was going on? Was this switching of motels some security rule? No. After a while I finally heard the story of why we stayed in the Quality Inn. It seemed that some of us had worn our welcome at the Holiday Inn.

Northrop was deeply involved with several "Black World" classified programs at the time. The crews supporting one of these large test programs at AEDC would always use one motel and crews on the other large program would use the other.

We were not supposed to be in town traveling for Northrop; we used fictitious company names like "Delta" or "Alpha" when we signed in at the motels. The only problem was we had been staying there for years, and everyone knew that we worked for Northrop.

"Good to see you all again. Now we are working for Delta (Wink. Wink.)."

Men who travel on business trips for long periods sometimes revert to their childhood days. There is often a lot of drinking, partying, womanizing, and horseplay. Finally, one of the boys told me the story of why we weren't always welcome at the Holiday Inn. I was not there on that trip. Stan Ton was one of the Model Mechanics who often went on wind tunnel trips with us. Stan was tall enough to stoop a little passing through a door and strong as an ox.

One night the crew was having a party in the Test Engineer's room at the Holiday Inn when there was a knock on the door. The boys were very jolly and welcomed anyone who wanted to join them, so they opened the door, but no one was there. Ok.

The knocking was repeated several more times and always there was no one there when they opened the door. Finally—a plan! Someone filled a wastebasket with ice and water and took up a post just inside the door with it in hand, ready to toss it on the pesky knocker. Another man waited with his hand on the door knob, ready to swing it open.

About this time, Stan decided to come over and join the party and knocked on the door. The door popped open and the bucket of ice flew out and hit Stan right in the face. One look at Stan standing there dripping wet and turning red in the face, and they slammed the door shut. Now the doors of the Holiday Inn are heavy, metal-clad doors but that didn't slow Stan down, not at all! A couple of loud crashes and the door was broken down, and Stan joined the party. They said it took eight guys to keep Stan from killing the guy with the ice bucket.

When I stayed at the Holiday Inn after that, I noticed the metal on the door to Room 227 was bent and twisted. After that incident, the Test Engineer's crew always stayed at the Quality Inn.

CHAPTER 21

The Test That Almost Wasn't

Northrop and McDonnell-Douglas companies teamed up to propose the F/A-18 fighter/attack plane to the Navy. The F/A-18 is a slightly larger, modified version of the YF-17 which had lost the Air Force competition to the General Dynamics F-16. The wings are larger and the landing gear larger and stronger to handle the rough carrier landings.

The F/A-18 8% scale force model was scheduled for a test in the 16T and 16S wind tunnels at AEDC. I was assigned as the Instrumentation Engineer. Ken was the Test Engineer, Mel the Designer, Stan Ton the Model Mechanic, and Earl Reade the Instrumentation Technician. While we were preparing the model for the test, we often piled into one car for lunch. One day we decided to go to the Officer's Club. The road to the O-club goes past a little pond full of turtles. Earl worked up a plan to get rich with turtle soup by disguising a boat as a giant turtle and sneaking up on them in the pond to catch them. However, this day there was a lone turtle walking down the middle of the road.

"Stop the car," said Stan. "I want to take that turtle back for my kids." Stan got out, walked over to the turtle and reached out for it. The turtle snapped at Stan and started running after him. Stan ran the forty feet back to the car with the turtle in hot pursuit. "Let's go! I think I'll get them another turtle."

Snapping turtles don't make good pets anyway.

At AEDC the models are prepared for testing in the large Model Installation Building. The test sections for the 16T wind tunnel are 40-feet long, tall as a two-story house, and as heavy as a locomotive. They are removable from the tunnel and transported to the Model Installation Building by a special electrically driven platform on heavy-duty railroad tracks.

The test section area is 16x16 feet so working on the model must be done standing on a 5-foot high platform. 16T has two test sections so that one model can be prepared for testing while another is testing in the tunnel. The model preparation went smoothly. The cart was brought to the Model Installation Building high bay area, and the sting adapter which fit our sting for the model to the AEDC support system was installed. Then our sting was mounted in the cart and the balance installed.

The balance was inserted into the sting and pushed into the socket tightly with push-on screws. These screws are prevented from backing out by welding thin metal strips over the screw holes in the sting. Then the balance block, which was the center piece of the model, fit snuggly onto the balance. The fuselage, wings, tail, etc. were attached to the balance block, and the model was built up piece-by-piece.

One or two days before the test currently in the tunnel would be over, I was inspecting the model. I noticed there was very little clearance between the little metal strips welded over the push-on screws and the inside of the balance block. I had Earl lift hard on the nose of the model. Under load the balance bent a little and the clearance at the back can get even closer. I was afraid the balance block might hit the sting which would mess up the balance measurements by producing another force pushing on the balance. I asked the AEDC people if the metal strips could be taken off, but they said it was against AEDC policy. If vibration caused the screws to back out, the model could come loose and go down the tunnel which would cause much damage to the tunnel and the model. The balance cost about $100,000, and we had over $250,000 in time and material in the model.

I pointed out the problem to the test engineer, Ken, and the designer, Mel. Mel checked the drawings and found the hole in the balance block was supposed to have been bored larger just where the balance ended, but it hadn't been done. It looked like the only way to fix it was to take the model apart and take the balance block to the shop for machining. There was only a day before our test was to start. This meant a bad delay. Ken and Mel went to tell the AEDC test engineer, and they were soon all in an emergency meeting.

I didn't have anything to do while the meeting was going on, so I just kept looking at the clearance problem and wiggling the model to see the gap change. The change was small for as hard as any of us could push on the nose, but the aerodynamic forces would be much larger. There were a lot of AEDC technicians and mechanics around, so I had one of them measure the gap with a feeler gage. Then I had them get a dial gage and mount it with a magnet to measure how much the gap was reduced when the nose was lifted.

That didn't look too bad, so I had the AEDC guys get a lifting strap or sling, a come-along and a tension meter. I set some other guys to removing two ceiling panels from the test section directly over the model. We put the sling around the model's nose, connected the dial tension meter to it to measure the force which we could pull up on the nose with. We connected the come-along to it, and attached the whole thing to a beam on the tunnel ceiling. With this setup, we could simulate the lift and pitching moment the model would produce during the test and measure how much gap we had left.

I had everything all set but didn't know how hard to pull on the model. I didn't know what the predicted model loads were. Ken would have to tell us that before we could begin our test, but the meeting was still going on.

And on.

And on.

And on.

Finally, everyone came over from the meeting to tell us to take the model off and send the part to the shop. I showed them what we had set up, and Ken calculated the maximum load for the model at that location. We slowly applied the load and measured how much the gap decreased. It was close, but there was still enough gap left at maximum load to give a safety factor for dynamics and model shaking. We closed up the model and got ready to run.

When the model was fully ready to run and all the screw holes filled with plaster, Earl and I did a final check on all the instrumentation. Uh-ho. One strain gage was open. When Earl asked Stan to take off the dorsal cover, Stan growled, threw a wooden stool against the wall, walked over, picked up the stool, stood on it and took the screws

Figure 36: AEDC technician with F-18 model in the AEDC 16-foot transonic wind tunnel.
Note all the holes in the side wall used to control shock wave reflections.

out of the dorsal, without saying a word. Earl and I just looked at each other. Earl found and fixed the broken wire, and Stan put the dorsal cover back on. It was ready to test.

After the test was over and the model disassembled, the balance block was rushed to the shop, and the bore was machined out as per the drawings to be ready for the next test.

CHAPTER 22

Duct Buzz by Any Other Name...

Another Northrop first— not only were we the first to have the Navy use AEDC to test the F/A-18 inlet/duct performance, we also were the first commercial company to test the inlet/duct performance of a company-funded aircraft, the Northrop F-20.

Yes, Northrop rented the 16T wind tunnel and broke it.

Figure 37: Northrop F-20. Note the large single tailpipe of the F-404 engine

The F-20 started life as an improved F-5 Freedom Fighter, the F-5G. The two J-85 engines on the F-5 were replaced by the much more powerful GE F-404 engine. The long inlet ducts on each side of the fuselage were joined together a little before the engine. This was called a "bifurcated duct."

Since this was to be a supersonic airplane, the shock waves in front of each inlet were to be stabilized using suction and a porous plate like that designed by Wilford Wong on the YF-17 and F-18. The main instrumentation were the forty Kulite probes that represented the face of the first compressor stage of the engine and the General Electric Analog Distortion Analyzer. This was my area of expertise, and the first test I supported as Possum Trot Engineering.

The two limits of the engine range of airflow are (1) "supercritical" where the airflow down the duct sucks the shock wave down the duct, and the duct flow is all supersonic and turbulent and (2) "Duct Buzz" where the duct airflow is so slow the duct acts like an organ pipe, and the shock wave travels up and down the length of the duct at the organ pipe frequency. This is like a man blowing across the mouth of a bottle, and it just sits there and "sings" on a particular note. Both phenomena only occur when the aircraft is flying supersonically, and they are easily recognized by looking at the signals from the Kulite transducers.

Our test was going along well, and the measured distortion was low. We would test the model at each pitch and sideslip angle ranging the duct flow from duct buzz to supercritical. Then Wilford noticed we were getting duct buzz when we were flying at 0.9 Mach- subsonically. You cannot get duct buzz subsonically! But here was our duct sitting there playing a steady high-C note. Impossible! Wilford could not bring himself to call it duct buzz. "It is some kind of an instability," he said.

My reply was "Wilford, duct buzz by any other name is duct buzz. If it walks like duct buzz and quacks like duct buzz, it is duct buzz."

It still went down as an instability.

The inlet system performed quite well. Distortion was low and would cause no problems for engine performance. The pressure recovery was a little low, but flow quality was good. Wilford concluded "the engine was just flying 5,000 feet higher than the airplane but that's OK."

We got daily reports of the costs being charged to Northrop. The printouts indicated there were about a hundred people charging to the test each hour that we were running. Ben, our test engineer and I decided to see if it seemed right. That's a lot of people! We started walking around the facility counting people. We also knew there were other people at other stations like the power substation and the water pump house around the base supporting us. We counted close to one hundred people— close enough for government work.

The test came to a sudden end with horns blaring, bells ringing, and a big "whoosh!" The 16T tunnel had an emergency shutdown. Ben, the test engineer, and I followed the AEDC test engineer downstairs to the motor room. 16T and 16S wind tunnels are both powered by a common driveshaft which is about 20-inches in diameter and can drive the compressors of either tunnel. This driveshaft, like a ship's propeller shaft, is kept continuously turning by a small motor to keep the shaft from developing a sag due to its great weight.

When the tunnel is started, the compressors are brought up to speed using two 18,000 HP asynchronous AC motors. Then two 40,000 HP synchronous motors are brought on line to get the tunnel up to the required Mach Number and dynamic pressure. That's a whole lotta horsepower!

The big motors are mounted halfway into the floor, and the top part protrudes above the floor greater than my height. Above each motor is a large discharge vent for

Figure 38: A portion of the drive system for AEDC 16S and 16T

a CO_2 fire suppressor system, which had gone off.

One 40,000 HP motor had some smoke coming out of it but no fire. We had burned out one motor or as we electrical engineers' term it, we had "let the smoke out of it." In a few minutes, a bunch of security guards came and swooshed us out of the area because of the CO_2 gas. They secured the building and let no one in again. That ended the test.

When I was a kid my Mom had the old wringer-type washing machines. I got several washing-machine motors to fool around with. The General Electric motors were held together with two long bolts that ran the length of the motor on the top and bottom and held the two end caps with the bearings in place.

The GE 40,000 HP motor at AEDC was built just the same. I think they just changed the scale on the original washing machine motors. One of these long bolts broke right behind the big nut that held it all together. The nut had fallen into the brushes, shorting everything out, and let the smoke out.

Luckily, we had gotten most of the data that we needed.

CHAPTER 23

Problem YF-23 Calspan Test

Shortly after I returned to Northrop in 1984, I was cleared on several ongoing Special Access Required (SAR) projects. SAR projects are called "Black World" projects which require special security clearances.

A YF-23 model was being tested at the Calspan transonic wind tunnel. There was some problem with the data, and I was sent to Buffalo, NY, to find the problem. Also, a classified part of the model had to be taken there which required a two-man carry. Such classified parts were double wrapped with the inner wrap labeled "Classified" and had to be constantly in the sight of the two people who carried it.

One-time Ron McCool, our tunnel operator, was sent with a female data technician to carry some classified material to Tennessee. Bad weather caused a layover, and they both had to stay overnight in a motel. The usual way to handle such a situation was for both couriers to share the same room and keep the classified material in sight of both. This wouldn't work in this case, both needed separate rooms. How could they both keep an eye on the package? They put it between the connecting doors of the adjoining rooms in such a way that neither could get the package without the other knowing it. They even had to place it in the bathroom door on the airplane where both could see it if either had to go.

Figure 39: Northrop YF-23

The aeroengineer who was accompanying me sat beside me on the commercial airline with the package under our seats. We were sitting there at 30,000 feet when he looked out the window and commented, "I remember the first time I took my hang glider over 20,000 feet."

"You did what?"

"Yes," he said "We would carry oxygen and ride the Sierra wave."

"You're crazy!"

"At first," he said, "glider pilots resented our flying up there, but soon they found the Sierra wave was marked with green, red, and blue squares of hang gliders, and they didn't have to circle around to find it. They were setting endurance and distance records by following the marked-out wave."

And people thought I was crazy!

When we got to Calspan, we were told the problem: all the Drag Polar plots had a discontinuity at zero. Drag polars are plots of lift coefficient versus drag coefficient. They indicate the minimum drag of an airplane and should always go smoothly from negative to positive lift values.

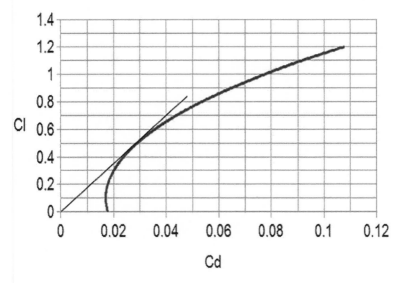

Figure 40: Drag curve for light aircraft.
$CD0 = 0.017$, $K = 0.075$ and $CL0 = 0.1$. The tangent gives the maximum L/D point.

The plots from this test took a large offset at zero. Calspan people tried recalculating the data manipulating the balance calibration coefficients in the data reduction matrix. They tried forty-four different matrices without success.

I asked about the calibration procedures and the data reduction matrix. I learned they had calibrated it using combined loads, a technique we did not use at Northrop.

This resulted in an inaccurate data reduction matrix. The problem is you cannot just combine the electrical outputs of the strain gages in the balance; you must convert the signals to force values first.

Calspan tried reducing the data with forty-one different matrices, arbitrarily juggling the values in the matrix. They used (6x42), (6x36), and (6x24) matrices but all gave bad drag polars. I suggested one more matrix, the 6x6 type that we used at Northrop. The drag polars looked ok with this matrix, but was the data correct? When I asked about the calibration technique and the matrix formula, I was told, "It must be right. A Ph.D. developed it."

That certainly did not reassure me.

We finally packed up five large boxes of test data printout paper, loaded them in the car and prepared to go home. On the way to the airport, we found a sale of a local beer, Genesee, at a liquor store. Unfortunately, the sale was only for the bottles, not cans, but the price was right, so we got a case to split when we got back to LA. We wrapped the beer like the data boxes and put it in with the boxes of paper and drove to the Buffalo airport. We checked our baggage and boxes in with a skycap. When he got to the case of beer, he asked, "What ya got here? Beer?" So much for our secret. He told us there was no guarantee if the bottles got broken. We agreed.

When we got back to LAX, we got all our bags and boxes from baggage claim except one We waited and waited, and then finally, long after all the other passengers had left, here came our case of beer sitting in a green plastic container. We gathered all our stuff, caught a cab, and went to Northrop in Hawthorne to lock all the data in a secure place in the project building. It was after 9 p.m. when we got there. After the data was locked up, we went out to our cars to divide the case of beer. Two bottles were broken— the glass was still in the dividers— but six bottles were missing. We laughed. The baggage handlers had a little party with our cold beer.

To resolve the problem with drag polars, we planned to install the Calspan model in the 7x10 wind tunnel using the same sting and balance as used at Calspan and see if we could sort out what had gone wrong and which data looked right from the Calspan test.

There was a rush to get the data straightened out, so we installed the next day. I checked the model after it was all installed and found that the model felt loose on the balance— the wings rocked as I pushed on them, and I felt a distinct "clink" as I rocked the wings.

Something was loose, and the first suspect was the balance pin which secured the model to the balance. By now it was second shift, and we were working on overtime. I called the model shop, which always had a second shift on duty, and they sent over a man to work on the pin. Everything was checked and the pin fit into both parts tightly. But there was still slop rocking the wings. The problem must be with the balance-sting joint.

We removed the model, and I examined the balance installation. Since the model was loose in the roll direction, I started checking the roll pins in the balance. Balances are held in place in the sting with tight-fitting taper joints, which lock together to prevent any slipping. Slipping in roll is also prevented by the tight slip fit of the roll pins used to align the balance. The roll pins go through the sting into small slots in the balance taper.

I found the pins were encountering the end of the slots as the balance was pushed into the taper by the push-on screws. This kept the balance from seating into the taper socket and allowed it rock around. This was easily fixed by grinding off some of the length of the roll pins to allow the balance to seat further into the socket. The disconcerting issue with this was all the parts, roll pins and all, were the same as were used at Calspan, and they had not indicated any mechanical assembly problems.

After grinding the roll pins down, we still found motion and slop in the assembly. So, we ground off more. No improvement!

The next step was to tear down the installation even further and pull the balance taper from the sting. The normal procedure to check the balance taper joint is to rub lipstick or a compound called "Prussian Blue" onto the male taper and see how much transferred to the socket when the joint is reassembled. This will indicate how much area is in contact with the mating surface of the taper. Our requirement was 80% contact.

When we pulled the balance and looked at the male taper, everything looked good. But when we investigated the socket, there were rough machining grooves all over the mating surface. The balance seated too deeply into the socket and rattled around in it. This was way beyond my ability to repair.

By this time, it was about one o'clock in the morning. We had been working on this all day and now we were stuck! I made a couple of phone calls, and by 2 a.m., I had every manager in the Aerosciences Lab in the tunnel pondering this problem. John Black, our best design engineer, remarked, "That sting is so rough that you could cut your finger on it."

It seems the sting had been sent to Calspan with the taper socket partially finished so Calspan could finish the machining and fit the sting to the balance (which already they had at their facility) properly. Apparently, they made a mistake and machined the taper in the sting too deeply. They then just assembled the sting, balance, and model and ran the test just as it was. Calspan is one of the best testing facilities in the country, and this was not the kind of work that I ever expected from them. No wonder we had bad drag polars!

We sent the sting to the model shop, and they cleaned it up as well as they could. The next day we were able to get a satisfactory fit with the balance, reassemble the model, and continue with the test. After the test, John Black had the sting cut up and a new sting made to the same specification as the original.

Our drag polars were just fine.

CHAPTER 24

YF-23 Dummy Sting Checkout

One of the problems with wind tunnel testing is determining the errors induced by the manner the model is held in the tunnel. At Northrop our preferred method was to mount the model on a balance attached to a straight sting that went into the rear of the model where the engine exhaust usually was. This meant the shape of the boattail of the model must be distorted to clear the sting. This caused some measurement errors which must be corrected for— especially for the accurate measurement of drag.

If you want to accurately model the boattail of the model, then the model must be supported in some other way. Often this is done by an offset blade sting going through the top or bottom of the model. Some tunnels have an external balance, and the model can be supported by three posts.

No matter what method of support is used, the proximity of the supports to the model always induces some errors. The engineers developing the YF-23 wanted to measure the effects of different mounting systems. The plan was to support the model with the sting up the rear, with a blade sting entering from the top and a blade sting entering the bottom. The blade stings would allow the model to have an accurate boattail.

Dummy stings would be used to simulate the effects of the sting in proximity to the model. These dummy stings would be mounted to the support system where the actual blade or sting would be but not quite touching the model. It was very important they not touch the model for then they would push on the model and mess up the aerodynamic forces measured by the balance.

When the wind blows on the model, the forces cause the sting and balance to bend and distort a little. Therefore, to determine the pitch attitude of the model, we always measure the angular bending of the sting and balance when we calibrate the balance. Then we can account for the sting deflections in the data reduction. We needed to measure the sting deflections more extensively for this test to ensure adequate clearances for the dummy stings.

We knew from experience the balances we usually use rotate ¾ degree about the aft side force gage flexure under full load. The rotation is not around the balance "center" but further aft.

However, the design engineer for the model personally directed measuring the sting deflections under load. He told us to place a single dial gage at the front of the balance and read off the thousands of an inch deflection as each 100-pound weight was loaded on the balance. He never said how he was going to use this data.

The B-2 division of Northrop had recently gotten in trouble with the Air Force by

Figure 41: Top-Blade mounted model (inverted)

Figure 42: Bottom-Blade mounted model

Figure 43: Sting-Mounted model

arriving at AEDC too often with the model only half completed and rushing to have the facility get the model ready to test, sometimes delaying the test.

My approach was to get as much work done on the model as possible before it was shipped because we had total control over the schedule of the Model Shop and other resources at home. For the check-out of this model, I insisted on having it in the Calibration Lab for one week before shipment to assemble it and check out the clearances with the dummy stings under loads. I ended up just having the weekend! That spoiled everyone else's weekend also.

It took several hours on Friday to assemble the model onto the test stand. The dummy sting had about 1/8-inch of clearance, but when we put on the first weight, the sting contacted the model, fowling the balance. I called the Design Engineer and the Model Shop.

"It shouldn't be fowling. I calculated the deflections."

Then followed a weekend of 12-hour days of taking parts off the model, milling out the part for more clearance, then putting it on the model and checking the clearances as we applied 100-pound weights up to the maximum expected loads. It took the Design Engineer, several Model Shop mechanics, the Test Engineer, two of my crew, and me to get the model ready to ship on time on Monday. I was so glad I had insisted on this checkout at home. What a disaster it would have been if we had waited until starting the test at AEDC.

The Design engineer, who had a Ph.D., came to us at first and told us he wanted us to mount a dial gage "there" and measure the deflections with the weights. If he had just come to me to tell me what they are trying to measure, we could have saved ourselves a lot of trouble.

This engineer said, "Just do it the way I said," so that's what we did.

He made assumptions which I could have told him were invalid. When you are trying to measure these kinds of angular deflections, you ALWAYS use two dial gages, one at the front and one aft, and measure the distance between them so the angle of deflection can be calculated.

That is why an engineer must never accept an order to "just do it this way." Always ask, "What do you want to measure and why."

The test went off at AEDC without a hitch.

CHAPTER 25

F-18E/F Afterbody Test or The Rear End Test

When we did the afterbody test on the F-18A/B we used a "flow thru" balance to measure the forces on the boattail of the airplane. This needed a special model because most of our force models had this area of the airplane distorted to insert the balance and sting. The forces on the rear of the model have a large effect on the drag. It was also required that the exhaust be modeled using heated high-pressure air.

The model was mounted on two long booms by the wings so the high-pressure air could by routed through them to each engine exhaust. The afterbody shell was mounted on a special force balance which allowed the air to flow through it. The problem was the air pressure also affected the balance measurements. These errors must be determined by pressurizing the entire plumbing system.

Another company designed and built the flow thru balance for this model. When we unpacked it from the shipping container, it was wrapped in dirty shop coats and the workmanship was very poor.

We calibrated the balance with various pressures applied to the system (statically with no flow). The calibration data was not very repeatable which made the accuracy limited. It especially failed to return to zero when the loads were removed. These poor "zero returns" were noted during the wind tunnel test, and the data had a lot of scatter.

When we started working on the E/F version of the airplane, I pushed hard to make the measurements by a different method. I wanted to determine the afterbody forces by measuring many pressures all around the afterbody.

We ended up measuring some eight-hundred fifty pressure taps on this model; all the flexible pressure tubing made the model look like it had been stuffed with spaghetti. 24-PSI pressure measuring modules were required to handle this. Luckily The B-2 Division had enough PSI modules and were able to loan them to us. It took two layers of PSI modules, each sitting on the other to fit all this instrumentation inside the model.

I insisted we build the model at Northrop and check out all the pressures before we shipped it to AEDC. I assigned our best instrumentation engineer, Fred Reinhart, to handle this big test along with a couple of our best technicians. I intended to send one other engineer with Fred when they went to Tennessee. It turned out when it became time to go, there were no other engineers available so I became the other engineer. So much for that plan.

Fred did a great job preparing the model. He was in charge of this test, and he knew the model intimately so I placed myself under him during the test. I was determined not to pull rank on him and to give him freedom to make his own decisions.

Figure 44: Wing mounted F/A-18E/F afterbody model in 16S wind tunnel.

Fred shipped out with the test crew to prepare the model for installation in the wind tunnel. I went later when the test was ready to go.

The first evening I got there, I noticed smoke as I climbed the stairs to the control room. It was pouring out of the door. I went in expecting to be met by firemen. It turned out to be coming from the microwave. Fred had really nuked a batch of popcorn. He spent the next hour scrubbing the oven.

On these wind tunnel tests everyone wanted to work nights to get the overtime, especially Sundays. We usually worked 12-hour shifts around the clock. To be fair they would usually switch shifts halfway through the test. This necessitated one crew would work a double shift— 24 hours straight.

I was always opposed to this practice for my men. I felt being that tired could lead to costly errors. I told Fred how I felt about this, however when the time came for the shop people to switch shifts, Fred allowed our technicians to shift also. Fred was in charge. I didn't say anything. As Admiral Halsey said to Admiral Spruance just before the Battle of Midway, "When you are in command, command."

The test went smoothly, and the data obtained this way was very accurate.

CHAPTER 26

"No Bill" Sign on the Model

I was having problems with calibrating the 5-component balance called the -89 store balance. This was a small Northrop-built balance designed to measure the aerodynamic forces on a bomb or tank carried externally on a model. Five balance forces are measured, all except the drag force. This would ensure that the bomb fell cleanly from the aircraft when dropped.

First let me explain that there is no such thing as a 3- or 5- component balance. ***All strain gage balances react to six components of force or moment.***

When all six forces or moments are measured with strain gages, the effect of each force component on the other forces which are called interactions can be measured and compensated for. If the balance is not designed and strain gaged for one or more components, the interactions act to increase the errors of the measurements with no way to correct for them.

Store balances are calibrated as installed in the bomb or tank they are used with. Ours are attached at both ends with taper fittings and aligned with precision roll pins. A properly fit taper joint will not slip under the normal loads applied to the balance, but each time I calibrated roll on this balance the tail fins on the bomb or tank were tilted when I finished. This meant "something slipped."

I checked the fit of the taper joint with the dye, "Prussian Blue," which indicated a "good wipe" with nearly full contact all through the taper joint. I had the model shop mechanics check everything and kept complaining to the model designer about the problem.

This test required several stores instrumented with −89 balances and all of them had this problem. But each time I re-calibrated the balance, the store rotated somewhere by 5 to 7 degrees, but both the taper and the roll pins should have prevented that.

I kept arguing with the model designer that something was wrong, and he kept saying everything was ok. I argued with my boss, Bob Lucas, who said that if the designer said it was ok, then it was ok.

"Get on with the calibration."

We agreed to reduce the roll load range and with lower loads and careful handling I was able to calibrate the stores successfully, and we ran the test in the 7x10 wind tunnel without problems.

My next encounter with the −89 balances came soon after. We were to test a TSSAM missile model in the 16-foot transonic tunnel at AEDC. The aero guys wanted to measure the loads in the vertical and horizontal tail surfaces. The model was designed and modified to use a 0.75-inch Task balance for the rudder and one of the −89 balances for the left horizontal. These balances had to be calibrated by AEDC using their data system and equipment.

The test was going well enough, but each time we shut down for a model change, I checked the vertical and horizontal to be sure they were tight. And each time I found the horizontal was loose and could be easily rotated by hand. The model mechanics kept checking for the problem and tightening them up for the next run. The next time we went into the tunnel it was the same thing again.

The mechanics thought I was being ham-handed when I checked them and was making them loose myself. I of course, knew better!

Finally, when I came into the tunnel to check them during a model change, I found a "NO BILL" sign with a large red circle and a red slash taped to the model. They weren't going to let me touch their model anymore!

Like heck! That was part of my job, and I was darned well going to do it. I complained to the test engineer who ran the test, and he supported my position.

Yep. The horizontal was loose again. Tighten it.

This continued for a few more runs. While I was watching the TV the model was running in the tunnel at high angle of attack, I saw the left horizontal suddenly rotate perpendicular to the airflow.

"Shut down. Shut her down!" I shouted. The horizontal might have been blown down the tunnel under the air loads.

When we disassembled the horizontal, we found the −89 balance non-metric end where it fit into the model was twisted like a pretzel. The way the balance was designed and built; the slots that engaged the two roll pins were cut clear through most of the length of the taper joint making a plus-shaped cut, looking from the end of the balance.

That made the small end of the taper so flexible it didn't press tight enough against the socket to hold it against much force. The roll pins held, but the four small parts were not stiff enough to prevent the balance from twisting in the socket and bending around the roll pins.

The problem was a poor design. After the test was over, we showed John Black, the chief designer, what had happened.

He had all the −89 balances sawn in two and several more built. This time the roll pin slots were only cut into the taper a short distance, leaving lots of meat on the inside area to hold everything rigid.

Problem solved!

CHAPTER 27

Minitunnel

We had a small "Minitunnel" located in a building near the main campus of Northrop. This minitunnel was part of our "Crabgrass Labs" concept for making it easy and inexpensive to get data on new concepts. It was a wind tunnel with a 14x20 inches test section powered by a four-foot diameter, chicken house ventilation fan. The idea was someone could come with a new idea and build and test his model hands-on with little support from the wind tunnel people.

We had a couple of ½-inch diameter balances which could measure 20 to 40 pounds of Normal force. The tunnel developed about 35 psf. (pounds per square foot) of dynamic pressure (q). We also had a small computer and data system which typed a line of reduced data each time "Enter" was pressed on the keyboard. Like the large 7x10 foot wind tunnel, the model could pitch from −15 to +90 degrees.

I particularly liked to harass my second level manager with the fact the minitunnel had "on-line" data reduction while the 7x10 had to reduce the data after the run was completed. Most other major wind tunnels around the country had on-line data reduction to allow them to make decisions while the tunnel was running.

Figure 45: Fan blades (Chicken-house fan) used at exit of Northrop Minitunnel.
Photo taken looking downstream from test section.

I used the minitunnel to develop the laser light-sheet system for the 7x10. I purchased a 9-watt Argon-Ion laser and assembled the optics to run that laser light through a fiber-optic cable and out a cylindrical lens to produce thin sheet of intense light vertically into the test section.

The output assembly was mounted on wheels like a little toy car and could be wheeled around to position it where desired. When smoke was sent down the tunnel over the model, the light-sheet would reveal a cross-section of the flow and show any vortices clearly.

We developed this laser light-sheet in the minitunnel, but it was designed to use in the 7x10 tunnel. While using it in the minitunnel, we found illuminating the model with a contrasting color of light, such as red light with a green laser, helped relate the illuminated flow with the model.

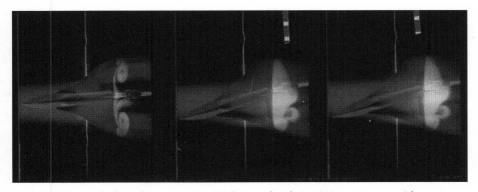

Figure 46: Laser light sheet photos of F-106 model showing the whirlpool-like cross section of the vortices. The left shows symmetrical flow at zero yaw. The pictures to the right show increasing yaw.

The minitunnel was great for getting a little data inexpensively for use in preparing a proposal for some new idea or project. On one test, we measured the loads on the tail fins of Mk. 62 bombs. There were thousands of these bombs in storage after Vietnam, and the military wanted to convert them to guided bombs by adding a guidance system and movable fins. The nose and tails of the bombs were replaceable and could hold the guidance system. The fin load data was used to try to sell the system in a proposal.

Another test involved installing two large fuel tanks under the wings of the F-20 fighter. The test engineers were a little crazy and a lot of fun to work with. Most under-wing stores are pointed directly forward, but we found if the stores were toed-in a little, there was less drag. We decided to name this toe-in angle "Ply" and gave it the symbol of the Gandalf G-rune. Thus, we tested 2-ply, 4-ply and 6-ply tanks.

Such was our weird humor.

Various engineers came in with ideas for better ailerons and control surfaces. They could test how well their ideas worked at low cost.

CHAPTER 28

The Gleeble

One researcher ran a material science laboratory at Northrop, and he was doing studies on the tensile strength of exotic metals. His laboratory was equipped with a large machine called a Gleeble. The Gleeble was made by Duffers Associates Incorporated.

It consisted of eight electronic racks along one wall which controlled a material testing machine which could heat and pull apart a small sample of the metal being tested. The specimen was inserted into metal jaws, heated by a large electrical current, and stretched by the jaws, measuring how much the material stretched under tension.

He was working with a material which underwent a phase change and changed resistance at a certain temperature. He called us in because any instrument he used to measure resistance was interfered with by the large 60 cycle AC current applied to heat the sample.

How could we measure the resistance accurately?

Two tiny wires were welded to the sides of the sample to measure the resistance. If these two wires were located directly across from each other, the AC voltage at each location would be equal and not cause interference. However, with such large currents, hundreds of Amperes, passing through the metal sample even the slightest misalignment produced several volts of AC voltage drop between the wires.

The system used to measure the resistance used a low voltage and produced small currents to measure the resistance. We would have to pick a tiny signal voltage out from a huge interfering signal.

The answer was to measure the resistance at a different frequency other than the 60 Hertz heating current. Then we could filter out the interfering signal and pass accurately the resistance signal. We chose to use DC voltage (0 Hertz) to measure the resistance and build a good 60 Hertz filter.

Warren Tribble and I built a 60 Hertz notch filter. It was called a T-notch filter and was a double filter, a low-pass filter and a high pass filter, tuned to reject only 60 Hertz. It was a simple network of capacitors and resistors whose values were calculated by formula. Capacitors and resistors only come in certain values, so we had to fine tune the filter in the lab to get maximum rejection at 60 Hertz. We spent quite a few hours fine tuning this filter to eliminate all the interference. Success!

Trib and I almost got ourselves into trouble years later with this 60 Hertz filter stuff. It just worked too well. One time, Trib was measuring dynamic pressures on a wind tunnel test at the Rockwell 7-foot Trisonic tunnel in El Segundo. He was getting a lot of 60 Hertz interference on his data, and we talked about building another filter to eliminate it.

Transonic wind tunnels have little slots all over the four walls to reduce shock wave interference affecting the model. They did a couple of runs with the slots taped over and the interference went away. It was not electrical interference but the real signal. This tunnel "sung" at exactly 60 Hertz. If we had filtered out the "interference," we would have filtered out the data we wanted.

You must be careful to know what you are doing!

CHAPTER 29

Electroaerodynamics or High Voltage Testing

This concept started with Mickey Cahn, the most innovative thinker I ever worked with. Mickey was totally "out of the box." In addition to being an Aerodynamist, Mickey was a comedian, musician, and inventor. In order to understand the advanced research we did you have to get to know Mickey a bit.

I thought his most useful invention was the mylar toothpick. Mickey took some of the mylar vellum drafting paper used by our drafting departments and cut it into one-inch squares. He bent each piece in half and packed them all into a small wooden match box.

Carried in your pocket, you could take one, fold it in half and use the corner to pick stuff from between your teeth. Used as a single layer, it passed easily between the teeth to get the deeper stuff. Then, you'd just throw it away. Very practical.

Mickey also did an act in a bar in the area. He would play a stand-up base fiddle while telling jokes. One time Northrop was preparing to build fuselage sections for the Boeing 747 aircraft and several Boeing engineers were in town to oversee the new assembly line at Northrop.

Several Boeing guys were in the bar when Mickey was performing, and Mickey happened to overhear them talking about the 747. After doing a few regular jokes, Mickey plucked a few strings on the base and said, "Now here is a very funny joke. I hear the drag-rise Mach Number for the Boeing 747 is only 0.82." The Boeing guys almost choked on their drinks and were totally amazed. Mickey added, "Also the rudder is going to be enlarged to increase its effectiveness."

This comedian knew things about the new airplane only Boeing personnel should know. After a few more jokes, Mickey told the Boeing people about his day job— a research Aerodynamist at Northrop.

I met Mickey when he came to the wind tunnel to get help to develop some of his ideas, and Bob Lucas pointed him out to me. Boeing was working on the Supersonic Transport and the big problem was sonic booms over populated areas. Mickey had some ideas he thought might solve this problem.

Sonic booms are caused by the shock waves from a supersonic airplane hitting the ground. The shock waves are made because the air molecules cannot get out of the way of a supersonic airplane fast enough and pile up on each other creating a pressure wave. Shock waves are created at both the nose and tail of the airplane causing the classic "double-boom" sound. They sweep back from the plane and travel with it. The boom goes along the ground at the aircraft's speed.

Since the boom is caused because the air molecules have no warning before the shock wave hits them, it seemed plausible we could reduce the shock strength if we could tell the air the airplane is coming so that it could start to get out of the way.

We cannot send a sound wave to warn the air because sound waves move at the speed of sound, and we are flying faster than that. But if we could warn the air of the airplane's approach with electricity, that warning would be sent at the speed of light. If we could put an electrical charge on the air molecule and on the airplane, then the electrical field could start to push the air out of the way before the shock wave gets to it. Maybe that would make the shock wave weaker.

We figured that could be done with a corona discharge which is created when a very high voltage is applied to a needle or sharp point. If the needle is charged negative, it will give extra electrons to the air molecules causing the air to become negatively charged. Corona discharges can usually be seen as a blue glow around the needle.

If the airplane is also negatively charged, the air molecules will be repelled by the like charges and start to move away from the airplane in advance of the airplane. That was Mickey's idea and we speculated it might solve the sonic boom problem. Mickey had the idea; I had the equipment available to test it. The lab I worked in had a 30,000-volt power supply, and I was later able to get a 100,000-volt supply. We started staying late after work and playing around with experiments to verify our theories.

One of Mickey's questions was, "Does a moving dimple create a wave?"

Mickey noticed if he created static electricity by rubbing a comb through his hair and brought it close to the surface of a bowl of water, the water would be attracted to the comb and rise a little. Then if the comb touched the water, the charge would be transferred, and the water repelled from the comb, causing a dimple in the surface. Was the shape of that dimple such that it would not make a wave if it was moved along the surface of the water?

Our lab had a "rate table" which was like a large record player that could spin instruments such as gyrometers around at different rates to calibrate them. We put Mickey's large salad bowl on this device, put water in it and used a 30,000-volt power supply to electrically charge a small rod placed near the surface of the water. Sure enough, if we touched the charged rod to the water, we got a dimple. We then turned on the rate table, and the dimple moved through the water as the bowl spun around under the charged rod. And, yes, Virginia, a moving dimple does make a wave! The wave in water would be analogous to a shock wave.

However, we did notice the wave in a rotating bowl of liquid did curl around upon itself and die out at a certain distance from the rod. Maybe if an airplane would fly a circular course vertically, climbing then diving, the shock waves would cancel themselves out before reaching the ground. It would not be very efficient, and everyone on board would get sick climbing and diving so much.

We had a 4-foot diameter rotary "water table" built from clear plexiglass. It had a 6-inch wide channel along the outside with 3-inch high plexiglass sides. A liquid placed in this channel would spin around and make nice waves from anything placed into it.

We could not only see the waves from above and below the table, but we could also view the profile and height of the waves through the transparent sides. We made a wooden boat-shaped model about 3-inches long with needles fore and aft. The needles were wired to our 30,000-volt power supply.

Water tended to short-out the voltage between the needles, so we filled the table with non-conducting transformer oil. We adjusted the rate table so the waves from the boat trailed back about 45 degrees, which is analogous to an airplane flying at Mach 2. As we applied the voltage, the waves would move upstream and spread out. The side view showed the waves were flatter and had smaller peaks. If this worked similarly in

Figure 47: The plastic rotary water table sitting on the rate table.
The model is in the transformer oil on the vertical strut held by C-clamps on the left of the picture.
The 30,000-volt power supply is on the floor behind the water table.

air, this would mean weaker shock waves and sonic booms.

If the table turned slower so the waves were almost perpendicular to the channel walls, corresponding to transonic airflow, the waves would completely flatten out and

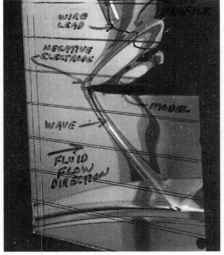

Figure 48: 0 Volts Applied

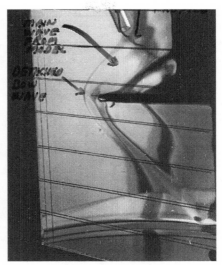

Figure 49: 30,000 Volts applied

Views looking up from beneath the water table showing
wave shapes with and without voltage applied.

could be seen moving upstream about halfway around the rate table.

The power required to do this was very small.

It was all very encouraging to us.

Now would this work in supersonic airflow?

Our lab had a small 5x5-inch supersonic wind tunnel which could be run in our Inlet and Duct facility. We set this up to run and built a model which I thought would work to demonstrate if our corona discharge idea would reduce the shock waves in air.

The model was a metallic cone with a needle affixed to its nose. This was held in the tunnel with insulating material and a wire was attached to the rear of the model to apply the voltage. The metal walls of the tunnel would be electrical ground for the power supply.

The wind tunnel was connected to a large vacuum pump downstream to exhaust the air which was supplied upstream by a 100 psi compressor. When the tunnel was running with the Mach 2 nozzle, the test section was in a strong vacuum. With the tunnel running, we applied the 30,000-volt power supply to the model expecting to create a pretty blue, glowing corona around the front of the model.

It didn't work that way.

What we got was a pretty glow running in the boundary layer flow around the insulating body of the model back to the back of the insulating mounting strut, then up the strut to the tunnel wall. The voltage never rose above 10,000 volts, but as I turned the control knob up, the brightness of the ionized gases increased as the current increased.

The system worked like an old-fashioned voltage regulator tube. Once the gases were ionized, the voltage was locked at that value, and any attempts to increase it only caused more ionization and increased current. Essentially, the metal walls of our wind tunnel shorted out our power supply at 10,000 volts, and we could not get enough voltage to produce the corona we needed in front of the model. This is the way the old voltage regulator tubes worked.

We tried several ways to insulate the inside of the tunnel— all to no avail. We were stuck; we could go no farther without building the wind tunnel out of insulating material, but we had bootlegged all our testing and had no money to have the shop build what we needed.

Mickey got kind of discouraged and decided to report on what we had done in the hope someone else could take the idea further. He wrote a technical paper for the American Institute of Aeronautics and Astronautics (AIAA) and presented it in New York City, arousing considerable interest and laughter. "Are you going to carry Hoover Dam behind the airplane?"

The next thing I knew, Mickey called to invite me to come to a press conference he was holding in the Engineering Building at Northrop. I came with Pete, the technician who was helping me. We both sat in the rear of the conference room guzzling coffee and donuts while watching the show.

Mickey was on the stage with his manager and a couple of other engineers. There were seven or eight people in the front rows of the audience, including reporters from the Los Angeles Times and the Aviation Week and Space Technology (AW&ST) magazine.

I imagine the conference was preceded by some VP in the corporate offices having received several phone calls that went something like this: "Yes. We have been working on this for some time. No, I don't know the current status, but I could have Mr. Cahn give you a call. Thank you. Goodbye."

Then to the intercom, "Carol, find out who the hell this Mickey Cahn is and what the hell he's been doing."

I think this conference was the result of several such calls.

The LA Times reporter asked the required question about Hoover Dam. Several other questions were fielded by Mickey, which he answered briefly.

Then Mickey looked down at the Aviation Week reporter and asked him, "What are you writing? Every time I answer a question, you write three pages of stuff."

"I'm a science fiction writer," he replied.

Someone else asked, "What is the current level of your research and funding now?"

Mickey replied, I'll let my manager answer that question." Mickey was standing on the stage and the others were sitting at a table on the stage. Before he stood up to answer, Mickey's manager slumped down like he was trying to hide under the table.

"This is a study which was undertaken some time ago. We have utilized company IRAD (Independent Research and Development) funds for much of the work Mr. Cahn has done. No government funds were available for research that is this advanced…"

Of course, we had bootlegged all this work, mostly on our own time and some using overhead funds for the labs. Nothing was officially blessed by Northrop Management.

The result of this news conference was Mickey mysteriously received $50,000 of IRAD (Independent Research and Development) funds for Electro-aerodynamic research. Here finally was the means to build our insulated wind tunnel.

Not quite.

Instead of just giving us the money to use to continue our work, we now had a board of company scientists to oversee how we did the research and spent the money. We were told we had to mathematically analyze the technique to see if it would work. So, we had several people study and write reports on various aspects of the subject.

Our argument was like the Wizard of Oz in the balloon: "We can't analyze it. We don't know how or if it works!"

This brings me to one of my pet peeves: Scientists today believe to discover something, you first need to analytically derive some theory, predict some phenomena that can be observed to verify your theory, and then observe the phenomenon.

Albert Einstein is one of my personal heroes. When he wrote both the Special and General Theories of Relativity, he mathematically predicted the change of mass when a particle travels near the speed of light and the amount that the light from a star is bent as it passes near a large star. Now everybody expects a scientist to predict something with their theory and to go measure it. They forget Einstein arrived at the Special Theory of Relativity to explain why an experiment failed.

In 1887 Michelson and Morey used a sensitive interferometer to measure the speed and direction at which the earth was moving through the "ether." The earth is whirling around the sun, the sun is speeding through the Milky Way galaxy, and the galaxy is zipping around relative to the other stars and galaxies.

They calculated their instrument should have been easily sensitive enough to measure how fast we are actually going. But, repeating their experiment over and over, they could not measure any difference in the speed of light whichever direction they pointed their apparatus. Bless these two true scientists because, unlike many today, they reported on their failure.

This caused Einstein to ponder, and he came up with the Special Theory of Relativity which explained that space shrinks in the direction of travel whenever an object nears the speed of light, and it shrinks just enough to make the speed of light appear the same in any direction relative to the fixed observer or an observer traveling with the object.

Thus, it is impossible to measure our absolute velocity through space.

But everyone forgets Einstein first observed an experiment, then he developed his theory, not the other way around!

All we wanted to do was experiment to see if we could affect shock waves with corona discharges. Then if we saw an effect, we could make some measurements and develop a theory to mathematically describe the changes we saw and use that to optimize the effect to perhaps reduce sonic booms.

The money kept slipping away and all we had done were paper studies, so we decided to go ahead and have the shop build a plastic non-conducting test section for our 5-inch tunnel. The top and bottom were made of one-inch thick phenolic and the sides were thick plexiglass. It was held together with nylon bolts.

The model was full-span, sharp like a razor blade both fore and aft. Screws on each side passed through a hole in the plexiglass and were used to connect to the power supply. The model was usually charged negatively. The other lead, usually the positive terminal, was connected to a pair of long needles pointed downstream in the nozzle area. Drilling through the plexiglass caused some optical distortion which shows on the schlieren photos but do not obscure the views of the shock waves. We made two test sections: one Mach 2 and one transonic test section.

Most testing was done at Mach 2. The 30,000-volt power supply produced no observable effects. I built a 4-foot long Tesla coil which was powered by my 120-watt ham radio transmitter. This worked best tuned to 1.8 megahertz, the lowest frequency it could be tuned to, and produced around 200,000 volts of high frequency alternating current. I was afraid to go into the test area when we were running and watched the schlieren picture via closed circuit TV, recording photos with a remotely-controlled 70mm camera.

Still, we had no effect on shock waves, but it sure was fun!

Figure 50: The Mach = 2 plastic wind tunnel with Tesla coil (long tube placed diagonally across the tunnel. The TV and 70 mm cameras can be seen also. I used TV to remotely control the tests. I was afraid to go in there when the voltage was turned on.

Then I dug up a 100,000-volt power supply which had been used on the X-21 Laminar Flow Control test aircraft. Dust and dirt often stuck to the front of the wing causing turbulent flow, and it was thought the dirt could be removed in flight by electrostatic repulsion. The airplane could be charged positively or negatively, and the ground lead of the power supply was connected to a long boom out of the tail with a sharp needle at the end of it.

Technicians told me when they ground tested it, the hair on their heads would stand straight up if they stood thirty feet behind the plane. They didn't want to go any closer.

Figure 51: Lightning bolts and plasma in plastic tunnel with Tesla coil

Using this power supply, we began to see some movement in the shock waves. I got a lot of pictures at Mach 2 showing the shock wave moving downstream slightly and appearing more spread out when the voltage was turned on. The current required was very small, a fraction of a milliamp.

We also measured the recovery total pressure downstream of the model and found the pressure was higher with the voltage on, indicating a weaker shock wave.

Our experiment was a success!

We repeated the experiment with the transonic test section. The shock wave was nearly perpendicular to the flow direction and when the voltage was applied, the shock moved upstream proportionally with the voltage, until it moved out of view of the schlieren system, at least three inches. The current barely registered on the meter.

We coined the term "Electroaerodynamics" for our technique of modifying airflow using corona discharges and electric fields.

We also tried some other applications for electroaerodynamics. At one time, Mickey tested a small wing in subsonic flow. The wing had a needle in front charged negatively and a metal flap charged positively. The flap was deflected so the airflow was separated from it in subsonic flow as observed by smoke.

When a voltage was applied, the flow stayed attached. This indicated we might be able to get more lift landing and taking off using electroaerodynamics.

I wanted to repeat that experiment in our low-speed tunnel using a force balance to measure how well it worked. I had the shop make a non-conductive wing about 3-feet in span with about an 8-inch chord from Styrofoam laminated with wood.

Instead of using a needle in front, I thought I would get better results using alternating strips of conducting paint on the top of the wing, each strip being charged alternately positively and negatively. It was mounted on a force balance and attached to the support system of the 7x10 tunnel and could be moved to any pitch angle.

Perhaps it was my idea of using strips of conductive paint rather than needles, but, try as I might, I could not measure any effect from turning on the voltage. That is, there was no effect to the lift of the wing or on the smoke. The effect I got was some sparking on the edges of the conductive paint which set the wing on fire. It was the only model I ever had burn up in the wind tunnel.

With the wing turned into a crispy critter, there was no way to repeat the experiment using other electrodes, so this part of our experiments was unsuccessful. However, I believe it may still be able to use electroaerodynamics to increase lift on wings at low speeds. Perhaps someone who reads this may be intrigued by our attempts and pick up where we left off.

We tried one other application for electroaerodynamics. Mickey Cahn had a friend who worked on the servo systems used to operate the gimbals that control the thrust vector of rocket motors of large rockets. This is an electro-mechanical system which has friction and lag. We thought applying an electric field to the exhaust of a rocket might be able to vary the thrust vector to give improved directional control.

Our problem was we didn't have any rocket motors to test with.

My suggestion was to use a model airplane Dynajet engine. These had been used for years for model airplanes but were banned in many states because models that got away and flew off could land and start fires. The Dynajet was a pulse jet engine like the engines that powered the V-1 Buzz Bombs to bomb London. It was about 18-inches long with about a ¾-inch diameter exhaust tube.

I mounted this on a force balance with a sensitive meter readout. I was looking for a change in side force as the voltage was applied to a pair of 2-inch square flat plates placed on either side of the exhaust discharge.

The fellow who sold me the Dynajet engine told me on the phone he once took his model to an airport where they were running up the engines on a couple of F-86 Saberjets. When he started his Dynajet, you could hear it clearly over the noise of the jet planes.

It was LOUD!

We set the test up in the back of one of the Inlet and Duct test cells with the engine exhaust blowing out the large back doors. A plastic lab bottle served as the gas tank so we could run for ten to fifteen minutes to get our data. The engine was started with a spark plug while blowing compressed air into the inlet. Once started it would run red hot until the gas was shut off.

One afternoon after we had finished testing, I went to my office to look at the data and left my assistant to clean up and secure the equipment. He told me some guy in a suit came in and started to ask him about out test.

"Are you the guys who are running that jet engine here?" He asked.

Pete replied, "Yes, but you need to talk to Bill Anderson or Hank Karazewski about it. They are the ones in charge."

"Do you realize the problems that you are causing with that engine?" He asked.

"No. You should talk to…," said Pete.

"You guys have to stop running that engine. Every time you start that thing up the noise runs down between these buildings to where the mechanics are working on the company airplanes. It is so loud they have to go inside and can't work on the airplanes," the stranger interrupted.

"You'll have to talk to Bill…," Pete said.

The stranger just continued, "Those guys are getting mad and they are going to just walk off the job pretty soon, and you know what that means, don't you?"

"No…"

"Well, you know that we just built a new building to build 747 fuselage parts for Boeing and the unions are trying to organize the workers to bring in the union to Northrop. And you know what that means, don't you?"

"Well, I don't think that would be so bad…," Pete started to reply.

"Not so bad?" Asked the stranger. "Look, if you guys keep running that jet, the mechanics will walk off the job and join the union. Then everyone on the 747 line will join too. Then there will be a strike which will stop our sending fuselage parts to Boeing, Boeing will not be able to deliver 747's to the airlines; Northrop will go bankrupt; Boeing will go bankrupt. The airlines will also all go bankrupt; the nation will fall into a recession, and you guys just have to stop running that jet engine."

After that he left, and we never saw or heard from him again.

We continued testing with the Dynajet engine without causing the collapse of the economy, but I could never measure any sign of thrust vectoring. I believe the pulse jet exhaust was not hot enough to ionize the gases so they did not react to the electric field.

We wrote a Northrop internal report and a technical paper for the AIAA describing our results. By this time, we had spent our $50,000 and had to stop our experiments. We accomplished what we had intended— we were able to modify shock waves using corona discharges. Now we hoped someone else would take what we learned and develop the concept further.

CHAPTER 30

My Last Dance at Northrop

In 1994 Northrop announced a "Golden Parachute" retirement plan with terms I could not refuse. I was able to retire at the age of 55 with my full pension. This meant everything I was working on had to be done by our Christmas vacation that year. That date coincided with the cancellation of the TSSAM (Tri-Service Stand-off Missile) program. The TSSAM program was plagued with problems and mismanaged for several years. Now that the program was about on track and having successful test flights and the program was being canceled.

They had just flown a test flight which had an engine failure they thought might have been due to ingesting some Magram— the rubbery radar-absorbing coating used on the missile. One of the managers in the program contacted the wind tunnel for help.

Rich Grimm and I went to see how he wanted us to help. For most tests, an engineer will contact us with a list of test conditions and model configurations he wants data for. This guy was different; he wanted us to tell him what to test and how to prove to the customer their improved Magram application process would hold up in flight. Rich kept asking him about Mach numbers, total pressures, and such, but this guy had no idea of these details. He just wanted us to tell him what to do.

Since I had run a consulting company and bid on several programs, I knew that this was a case where the customer was asking the bidder as the expert to give a detailed proposal on how they would solve his problem. This was a great opportunity for a contractor to propose a good solution. I took Rich aside and explained this different approach to him and said we would tell this guy exactly how to run his test and the conditions to test. Since the concern was Magram had broken off the inlet lip and been swallowed by the engine, Rich and I went to see an expert in inlet design, a guy named Gordon. The TSSAM project was still classified SAR (Special Access Required) and Gordon was not cleared on the project, so we could not go into too many classified details.

Gordon turned out to be the perfect guy to go to. He had worked on the TSSAM project at its start but now was debriefed from the project. He designed the inlet and explained it was designed with the stagnation point well inside the throat so any Magram that might come off the lip would not enter the inlet but be blown out. The stagnation point is the place where the airflow divides and part of it enters the inlet and the rest of the air goes outside along the missile.

We all put our heads together and decided on two tests to recommend. One was to test the new application process by blasting a test sample with something like a sand blaster at certain angles and velocities to see how it held up. The Engineering Test Labs had the equipment to do this, so they would conduct that test. We all had to hurry because the end of the year was coming soon, and the project would be canceled and many of us would retire.

The other test was to place the section of the missile fuselage which included the inlet and duct in our Inlet and Duct Facility test cell and run under conditions similar to cruise conditions for longer than a typical mission. This would entail blowing air over the entire test article and sucking air through the inlet and duct.

Our I&D Facility had two large compressors, the primary pump which could suck or blow large quantities of air and the secondary pump which was smaller and only sucked. For years the primary had been only used to provide suction. It seemed I was the only one around who remembered that the primary could blow too. The mechanics had to study the plumbing to see how to switch the system over. A blank plate could be moved from the suction end to the pressure end to connect the compressor exhaust to the pipes in the test cells.

Since the system had not been run in this configuration for some time, we decided to do a couple of cleanout runs before installing the model. We opened the 16-inch pipe where we would mount the model and fired up the primary. It ran with a loud rattle. The operator, opened the valve and a large cloud of dust and rust blew out of the pipe. It filled the whole test cell with dust and small scraps of tape, paper, bolts, and other stuff that had been sucked into the system over the years. As I watched, an entire roll of duct tape came popping out and rolled across the floor.

This was a real "clean out run."

We swept up all the dust and had the model brought down for installation. It was a classified SAR (Special Access Required) model so security came and secured the building and had a security guard control door access 24-hours a day.

The I&D had a large roll-up door that could be opened using a hand chain or an electric motor. They put a padlock on the chain so it could not be used to open the door. Once again (we had been down this road before) we pointed out the door could be opened by pushing the button to turn on the roll-up motor. They didn't care. "This is the way our instructions say to secure this building and that's how we are doing it." Ok.

We installed the model and blew air over and through it at various velocities and conditions. We tested for several hours, much longer than a TSSAM flight and no Magram blew off. Thus, the new Magram process worked properly, and the test was successful.

This testing ran until the last day before our Christmas vacation. We tested until noon that last day, then pulled the model, sent it back to the program area, unsecured the area, cleaned up, and went home.

On January first, after Christmas vacation was over, the TSSAM program was canceled and the retirement for several of us, me included, became effective.

End of test, end of project, end of job. Now I can sleep in!

CHAPTER 31

My Longest Wind Tunnel Test

I retired from Northrop December 31, 1994 at the end of my Christmas vacation. For about 25 years I had been responsible for the Calibration Lab at the wind tunnel and for the wind tunnel balances we owned. I had 17 Task/Able balances under my control, each worth around $100,000. All the aerospace companies and wind tunnel facilities would borrow and loan balances as needed, each promising to repair any damage during their use.

As a result, as I neared retirement, I was contacted by engineers from McDonnell-Douglas in Huntington Beach, CA. They wanted to borrow one of our small, 0.5-inch Able balance for their upcoming Delta III rocket test. I got all the paperwork done for the loan before I left Northrop. They told me they needed an engineer for this test and suggested I consider "job shopping" with them for the test. They even said, "I should ask for a high salary because they would pay whatever I asked."

It sounded good to me, and as soon as I was retired, I applied to them and was accepted. I was in negotiations with a government agency to buy the house I was living in at auction and was short of cash, so I did not ask for too large a salary lest the deal fall through. I soon headed to Huntington Beach to meet my new boss and his engineers who were working on the rocket modifications and to see the model. I was there to replace a technician who had worked on the model for years and had to retire. We all went to the warehouse and pulled out the cases which contained the model.

It had been first built as a Delta II rocket in 1963, the year I started at Northrop and been tested and modified many times since. Assembled, it was about 5-feet long. There were a million tiny parts, each held on with tiny 0-80 or 2-56 Allen head screws. The screws were packed by pushing each one into a piece of Styrofoam, color coding each one "red" for the front or "black" for the rear and marking the Styrofoam with the name of the part which they fit. Each screw had been individually ground to its proper length because the wall of the model body was thin, and the parts were small. They told me this goes here and that goes there. This was going to be a large 3-dimensional puzzle to put together.

They gave me an office, and I began to make drawings of the new parts that were to be used for this test. The Model Shop in St. Louis would fabricate the parts, and I would go to St. Louis early to assemble the model for the test. There were two models to be tested during this test— a force model and a pressure model. The force model had been originally built for a 1.5-inch diameter balance but had a sleeve installed to fit the 1.25-inch balance that we would use.

As I fit the model together, I discovered it had been used so much the sleeve was worn and loose on the balance. I had the shop mechanics replace the sleeve and lap it in for a good fit.

The metal pressure tubes were short, and I feared the bundle of flexible tubes attached to them would get pinched because there was not much room to run them through the model out to the pressure modules. The technician before me had made it work before, but I suspected I would have trouble that way, so I had the shop solder

Figure 52: Delta II

steel extension tubing to each one to get the tubes past the pinch points.

Another problem I was concerned with was starting loads on the force model. When a supersonic wind tunnel is started, a shock wave travels down the tunnel. As it passes over the model, sometimes for a few milliseconds, the flow may be supersonic over the top of the model but not over the bottom. This can cause very heavy forces on the balance for an instant.

I had to estimate these loads to ensure the balance was not overloaded and broken. My estimates indicated these starting loads could indeed overload the balance. The pitching moments especially could be high.

Force models are usually tested with a layer of copper tape or "fouling strip" wrapped around the sting at the rear of the model. It is wired to an alarm to warn if the model is touching the sting and fouling up the force measurements. I put a fouling strip on this model also but every time we ran in the tunnel, the starting loads were so large all the tape was worn off by the back of the model banging around against the sting.

In this case, that was a good thing. Instead of these large forces being carried by the balance, they were transferred to the sting by this contact thus limiting the balance loads and saving the balance.

Whew!

The 1/2-inch balance I loaned to these guys before I retired was used to measure the loads on the strap-on booster rockets. Delta II rockets had seven solid rocket boosters to give them more thrust to launch heaver payloads.

As the booster rockets burn out, they are jettisoned off. The model boosters are mounted at various angles and positions near the main rocket where they should fly away safely as they separate from the rocket. Only one booster has the balance which measures the forces to ensure it will clear the rocket safely. The model was rotated to the position of each booster rocket to check how each booster would clear the rocket.

I was a one-man test crew on this test. First, I installed the models and made all model changes between runs. Also, I set up the run schedule and optimized the order of runs to get the most runs each day. We were testing in the McDonnel-Douglas 4-foot blowdown supersonic tunnel, which used large tanks to store air at 600 pounds per square inch (psi) as an air supply. The tunnel used up all this air during each 1-minute or so run.

During this time, the model must be pitched to each angle, which is to be tested, and data recorded at each angle. Then the air bottles must be pumped back up to 600 psi, which took two to three hours. This gave me enough time to make model changes between each run, even big model changes.

The Mach number in supersonic wind tunnels is dependent upon the tunnel nozzle area. This tunnel had a nozzle made of flexible steel walls which could be flexed by electrically-controlled jack screws which are moved in or out to change the nozzle area and shape.

There were ten or twelve jack screws on each side of the tunnel, and any one was likely to jam when it was moved to change Mach number. It could take hours to fix it and could seriously delay the test, so we had to work the run schedule and model changes to minimize Mach number changes.

Normally we would do all the runs on a model configuration together, but now I had a lot of time to make model changes as we pumped back up. That was better than jamming up a nozzle jack. It was a lot more physical work for me wearing my Model Mechanic's hat, but it was the most efficient way to conduct the test.

Most of the force model portion test went smoothly, but one time when I was making a model change St. Louis had a thunderstorm and it started to rain— on me and my model!

Directly over where the model sat when pulled back from the tunnel was a roof vent. It had louvers to close it off when the fan was not running, but now it was stuck open and the model was getting wet. Water could mess up the wiring and the balance, so we wrapped the model in plastic and ran it back into the tunnel. After an hour's delay, I finished the model change and we continued testing.

This was the only test I was on that was delayed by inclement weather.

When we got to the pressure model portion of the test, I made a bad mistake. I allowed the tunnel people to mount the PSI pressure measuring modules further back in the tunnel where they were easier to work on. I should have had them mounted just behind the sting with shorter pressure lines.

Everything worked fine at first, but we had a few runs planned at Mach 4 and 5. The trouble was at Mach 4 and 5 the air is less dense, and it takes longer for the pressures to settle to their new values after each pitch change.

The Aero guys saw something looked wrong with the data. So, we had to rerun those runs and finish the series pausing longer at each pitch angle to let the pressures settle. We had to break each run into two parts to get the data before we ran out of air.

My guys were not very happy with me! I should have known better— I had spent my whole career working pressure lag problems.

We finished, packed up, and went home after a long four and a half months.

CHAPTER 32

Skunk Works

A couple of years after I retired, we had a reunion Christmas party at the wind tunnel at Northrop. Walt, the former manager of the Design Group, told me that people at the Lockheed Skunk Works were looking for wind tunnel test engineers. I called Walt's friend and soon I was on my way to Palmdale, CA, to start another job-shopping job.

I was directed to a large group of modular buildings where Lockheed was working on developing their entry to the Joint Strike Fighter (JSF) competition. This airplane was to be three variations of one design adapted for the Air Force, Navy, and Marines. The three versions were labeled for where they landed and took off: "A" for asphalt (USAF runways), "B" for beach (Marines vertical takeoff and land (VTOL)) and "C" for carriers (Navy).

Northrop tested some preliminary ideas for this requirement before I retired. We tested a version that had a small jet engine mounted vertically just behind the cockpit for the VTOL "B" version. Only Boeing and Lockheed were selected for further development to produce two prototypes. I was to work on this development labeled the X-35.

When I arrived at this huge building, I was directed to a conference room where my new boss was holding a meeting. I entered the room and sat down quietly. Jim headed all the aerodynamicists for the X-35. Several of his aero guys just returned from a briefing with the customers at Lockheed in Fort Worth, TX.

Figure 53: F-35 Joint Strike Fighter

One man explained they told the customer some wind tunnel data showed some lateral instability. They explained they thought it was due to the way the inlets were faired over and would not be seen on the actual airplane.

The Lockheed people at Fort Worth loudly complained they should not tell the customer there was a problem. These were the same people who lost the A-12 contract a few years earlier because they covered up problems and cost overrun.

Jim asked whether that was true, then said, "If you tell the truth, you will never get in trouble with me. I will always stand behind you."

I thought right then, "I'm going to like working here." I met all the guys I would be working with and was briefed on what we would be doing.

The first project I testing was the VTOL "B" version for the marines. The airplane had a main jet engine whose exhaust could be directed downward for vertical take-off. There was a Lift Fan behind the canopy driven by a shaft from the engine. Roll control was achieved by a small jet under each wing which was fed by engine bleed air. All four jets were supplied on the model by large flex hoses connected to high pressure air supplies through control valves.

Previously I have discussed the difficulties of getting accurate measurements using

Figure 54: F-35 Take Off

high pressure air on metric models like we did on the YF-17 Afterbody model. The pressure of the air in the hoses cause them to push on the balance and cause errors. On the F/A-18 Afterbody model, we measured many pressures in lieu of a force balance.

For this model, Lockheed attached the air hoses to a large circular center section of the model which was rigidly attached to the sting support. All four jets were rigidly attached to the center body. Each jet was connected to its own air supply. The balance was attached to this center body too, but the rest of the model was built around it, without the model touching it.

Thus, the balance would measure only the forces generated by the air blowing on the wings and fuselage of the model. The forces generated by the jet nozzles were calibrated separately. This was a very clever solution to the problem.

Since this was a VTOL aircraft, it could hover or move slowly sideways or backwards. Therefore, the model had to be mounted in the tunnel backwards and at other yaw angles.

This was accomplished by loosening the top part of the center body and rotating the model under it to the next setting every 15 degrees. Tightening it again sealed the pressure chambers in the top with the chambers in the bottom. Sometimes one chamber in the bottom rotated to another one in the top chamber which shifted the air supplies to different nozzles.

One night I came in and the Tunnel Operator said, "Do you know that your model is in the tunnel backwards?"

One quirk of this model was that the balance was mounted upside down and backwards. The end of the balance was normally attached to the sting which was attached to the metric part of the model, and the model part was attached to the center body. Up was also down.

The data reduction program NASA used was designed to accommodate any balance orientation. You only have to tell it which balance axis was aligned to which tunnel axis. X is changed to $-Z$ or $+X$, etc. But nobody could figure out which way was up.

Engineers are taught in college to visualize a right-handed coordinate system by pointing the index finger of the right hand in the X direction. Bend the middle finger 90 degrees and it points in the Y direction and the thumb points up in the Z direction.

For three weeks everyone in the Control Room walked around with three fingers pointed in three directions, pulling one of them toward another finger and mumbling, "X goes into $-Z$ then Y goes into X."

They never did get it right.

We went through the whole first test without getting good force data. Luckily, Lockheed was building a new model, similar in design but the balance fit into it normally.

The test was run in the 14 x 22-foot VTOL tunnel at NASA Langley in Virginia. When I got there, it started to look kind of familiar. This was where I had gone years before on my first off-site wind tunnel test. That first test had ended when one of the large jack screws in the pitch system broke.

This first Lockheed test here ended the same way— the same jack screw broke. Outside, I found a 4-foot high heap of broken jack screws piled against the building, rusting. There must have been over fifty of them, each one must have been quite expensive. They had just been breaking them for twenty years.

Some things never change.

As soon as I arrived, I got a call from the boss. The wife of one of my engineers had gone to the hospital. As soon as Tom got there, I turned him around and sent him back. Our crew was now short one man.

Lockheed also arranged to send an old friend named Larry from their Marietta, GA, facility to help me with this test. Larry had been one of the Test Engineers I worked with at Northrop before he went to Lockheed. He was a great guy and a big

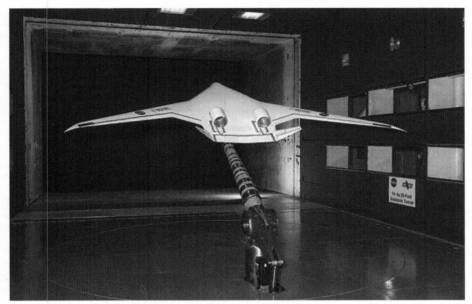

Figure 55: Langley 14x22 foot test section with a blended-body model

help on this test. The test went along smoothly. All systems worked well except for the balance orientation problem.

Lockheed was competing with Boeing for the Joint Strike Fighter (JSF) contract, and our model and data were classified "proprietary." I was told to restrict the number of people that could see the model to a minimum.

NASA was developing a new system of measuring the pitch, roll, and yaw angles of the model by mounting several Light Emitting Diodes (LEDs) on the model and tracking them with TV cameras. They asked me if they could try using this system on our test. I said, "No." I didn't want extra people to have access to the model.

This resulted in a couple of phone calls from NASA to the Project Office in the Skunk Works. I got a quick call from home to let them use our model for their testing. "OK. No problem." I had maintained security properly.

Things went along nicely until suddenly the pitch system stopped working with the model pitched high in the tunnel.

Guess what??

The big jack screw broke where it was turned down to fit the upper bearing, just like it did to stop my first test there over twenty years ago.

End of this test too. I looked outside. Along the back wall was a large heap of broken jack screws.

Calibrations

While the new model was being built, I was sent back to Langley to calibrate the jet nozzles we were using. NASA had a flow facility with an accurately calibrated venturi that could measure the mass flow rates plus thrust and rake pressures of each nozzle. It was a two-man job— just me and one technician to help set up the test articles and run the systems.

The calibrations went smoothly. I calibrated each nozzle, lift fan, both roll nozzles, and the vectored main jet nozzle throughout its entire range of settings.

The facility was great. Each data point was plotted in the computer screen right after it was taken. It was easy to see if the data was good right away.

We had to run using two venturi, a low range and a high range. There was some overlap in the ranges of each and the two curves did not match. The error was small but larger than the quoted accuracy for the venturi. I mentioned this error to the NASA manager, but there was nothing they could do about it at this time.

At one point, this manager called me to his office. He was the manager responsible for several wind tunnels including the 14x22-foot tunnel we were testing in. This tunnel was very busy because both Lockheed and our competitor, Boeing were testing their JSF versions there.

He read me a letter he had received from Boeing that explained Boeing understood NASA's scheduling problem, and they were going to help them.

It said, "It will be a cold day in Hell before we ever test there again."

I guess Boeing was having the same kind of troubles we were having getting data and support from the tunnel.

This manager told me he didn't want to get a letter like this from Lockheed and urged me to work closely with him if I had any problems again testing there. I assured him I would do my best, but I could not control what my management might do if things did not go well.

Testing the New Model

After the tunnel pitch system was repaired, I took the new model there for more testing. NASA had re-engineered the pitch system (after all these years) to solve the problem of breaking jack screws.

The new screws had larger, stronger ends to fit into the bearings at the top and bottom. They never did break during our tests, but the bearing assemblies they used were only designed for upright mounting. The top bearing had to be mounted upside down and leaked grease constantly. It had to be re-greased after each run.

How did we ever get to the moon?

The new model was designed like the old one, but the balance mounted normally and that solved that previous problem. Our run schedule included ground effect tests where the model was lowered to ½-inch from the floor of the tunnel. This distance was hard to judge from the control room, so we rigged a laser pointer to hit the main landing gear wheel at that point. One TV camera was rigged to monitor that area when we had to do those runs.

My test crew included one lady engineer and one other engineer who seemed to resent her. Also, one of the facility technicians kept trying to hit on her so I had to act as a mediator on personnel problems. That is what test engineers do.

When the lift fan and main jet were directed downward and hit the floor strongly, they created a strong sheet of up flow where the two jets hit each other and forced the flow to blow up. We were to try to find ways to enhance this effect to get extra lift on the aircraft.

We tried various configurations of doors and fences to trap more of this up-flow. After every run, we were laying on the floor attaching steel plates to the bottom of the model and taping over the cracks. These were mounted using #8 screws at first, but after breaking several, we enlarged them to #10 screws.

Testing these ideas showed some improvement but not enough to offset the extra weight of the doors and actuators so it was not used of the aircraft. One difficulty in this kind of test is determining the air speed. We would like to simulate in the wind tunnel the speed of the aircraft moving through the air. The jet air blowing around under the model blocks some of the wind tunnel air from passing under the model, forcing it to go over the top of the model. This reduces the effective area of the test section causing the air over the top of the model to move faster than the speed that the tunnel was set for.

Wind speed is usually measured by measuring the difference between the ram air pressure (pitot pressure) and the static air pressure. We measured this accelerated air speed by mounting a pitot-static probe to the ceiling. Our model had four large high-pressure hoses attached to the top of the model. These looped up over the model, then were bent down to run along the sting. The tunnel operator had to be careful to not raise the model too high in the tunnel or the hoses would wrap themselves around the pitot-static probe and twist it into a pretzel.

One time after a series of runs, another engineer and I were in the control room and heard a loud "thump." The operator had been moving the model around near the floor.

"Did you hit the floor," she asked.

"No," the operator replied. We went into the test section and saw the both landing gears had been bent 45 degrees to the outside.

Oops!

This first test on this model went smoothly until the tunnel operator let the smoke out of a 10,000 horsepower DC generator. At very low air speeds, the fan was turned using a DC motor-generator set to get finer control. He would shut off the DC system and switch to an AC motor for higher speeds. He had been usually the operator of another wind tunnel but was brought in here because of the tight tunnel schedule required for JSF testing.

He forgot to turn off the DC system and burned out the DC generator, or as we electrical guys say, "He let the smoke out of it."

When you let the smoke out of an electrical system, it doesn't work anymore. This marked the end of this test while they sent the generator off to Chicago to be rewound.

NASA Ames Ground Plane Test

This airplane was designed to land and take off from the decks of aircraft carriers and ships. It was important to measure the temperature and pressure of the jets impacting the ground or deck. It would not be good to dig a crater landing on the ground or to melt part of the deck of a ship. The landing pads on ships and carriers are carefully designed to provide cooling for each individual VTOL aircraft. We measured these temperatures and pressures using a large ground plane with the model mounted in the world's largest wind tunnel— the NASA Ames 80x120-foot low speed tunnel.

It wasn't really a wind tunnel at this time. Earlier when my boss was working there, he tried to get a little more speed out of the fan system there. Air speed in this tunnel is provided by a large bank of many fans forming the back wall of the tunnel. The fans had wooden propellers and wooden louvers that could be adjusted to slow the air speed.

Jim kept opening them more and more until they went over center, and the wind blew them backwards, breaking them and sending the pieces through the fans, breaking the fans also. NASA was waiting for new fan blades to be built. Thus, it wasn't a wind tunnel. It was just a big room we could mount and move our model in.

The ground plane was a steel platform about 20x20 feet mounted on legs which raised it about twenty feet above the tunnel floor. It had numerous pressure-taps and thermocouples mounted at various locations. The model (the same one we had tested at Langley) was mounted on the tunnel support system so it could be moved down near the ground plane at various pitch angles. It was supplied with heated high-pressure air like at Langley.

The next test scheduled to come here was a test of a full-scale Wright Flyer built by my friends in the American Institute of Aeronautics and Astronautics (AIAA). Since I was there, I was able to coordinate planning for that test also. We had to use a high-lift platform to lift us thirty to forty feet in the air to make model changes. That was different!

This test went well. We had to test at night, and some of those nights seemed very long. It can be boring just sitting there while the tunnel runs. One evening we went to a Chinese restaurant. One of the fortune cookies produced our motto for the test, "A delay is better than a disaster." Amen!

The Ames test went smoothly, and we got good data. Incidentally, the Wright

Flyer test which followed us was a success also. It proved the Flyer was an unstable aircraft, but Orville and Wilbur were great pilots.

Lockheed invades England

The last test I went on for the Joint Strike Fighter was to the Land of Wrong-way Drivers— England. We were to test the F-35C, the navy version, in the 15-meter pressure tunnel in Farnborough. This tunnel's test section was entered by passing through two turnstiles, like entering a subway or Disneyland. This kept track of whether you went through the outer one first or second. If you went through the outer turnstile first, it knew you were going in. If the other turnstile was first, you were on your way out. If the goings in did not equal the goings out, you were getting locked in and going to be killed. Safety first.

I was kept busy planning model changes, taking photos of each configuration and overseeing each run. One time, I gave the model mechanics the wrong configuration to install on the model. I ran from the control room to the tunnel as fast as I could. When I ran through the turnstiles, the second one did not unlock fast enough, and I slammed into it with my leg. It turned all black and blue and hurt like heck. I could not wait until the shift was over, and I could go back to my hotel room and soak it in the tub.

It was late when I finally left and tried to find my way over the English road system to my hotel in Basingstoke. I knew to drive on the left side of the road. I looked right, then left then right again. I pulled out into traffic and "BAMB!" I was hit by a lady in a car that I hadn't seen. Nobody was hurt, but I spent the next three hours in the local police station with a very nice constable. Finally, I got to soak in the tub and it sure felt good.

The next day my leg was so sore I decided to test the British healthcare system and went to the hospital. I can report I got taken care of in a timely and adequate way with no cost. While I was waiting, an old man came into the hospital through the automatic doors. Apparently, he got second thoughts and turned to leave when the door swung open again and knocked him down. They carried him away on a gurney. I guess they needed some more business that day.

I had scheduled my departure to give me a couple of extra days to see some of England. One day I went to Salisbury and saw Stonehenge and the tree where my favorite author, J.R.R. Tolkien sat and got the idea for his hobbit stories. It was a beautiful place.

The next day, I went to see the air museum at Duxford during a full-blown blizzard. The museum was housed in five large hangars spread along the runway for about a mile. They were not heated. In the U.S. and especially at Chino, CA, which is near my home, we had many P-51 Mustangs. At Duxford they have a plethora of Spitfires and Hurricanes, which are somewhat rare here in the United States.

It was wonderful seeing all the unique aircraft in various stages of restoration. Each large hangar had many rare British aircraft sitting around that I could see up close. Occasionally, as I walked through the quiet hangars, I come across one or two workers cleaning or refurbishing some part of an old airplane. Most planes were World War II era. I would see all the planes in one hangar, then freeze my way through the blizzard to the next hangar. The last place was a museum dedicated to the sacrifices of America in defending the United Kingdom.

Prominently hanging from the ceiling was a huge B-52 jet bomber. This building contained examples of the many American aircraft used in WWII. What impressed me most was the transparent fence outside the building. Each pane had dozens of little pictures B-24's, B-17's, P-51's etc., representing a plane and crew lost during the war. There were thousands of them! Many carried crews of ten or more people.

I made it to Heathrow airport the next morning and flew home.

The Last Test

My last test for Lockheed was a store separation test at Arnold Engineering Development Center. AEDC's 4-foot transonic tunnel has a special setup to measure the trajectory of a bomb or missile as it is launched from an aircraft.

I was once taking a tour of AEDC and they showed a film of an F-15 releasing a 500-pound bomb. The bomb just loved that airplane. It didn't want to leave it. It flew in formation with the F-15 for over a minute, occasionally kissing the bottom of it and knocking several small pieces off each time. The man showing the film said, "That is why we have AEDC."

The rig in 4-T has a dual support system. One holds the airplane, the other holds the bomb or missile. Six components of force are measures for each so the motion of each can be calculated. The bomb was placed just under the aircraft model but without touching it. The forces on both are calculated and the relative positions where each will go a fraction of a second after release is calculated. The models are moved to that position and the forces recalculated; then the models are moved to the next position, etc. This is repeated until the complete trajectory of the bomb is calculated.

Our test was to ensure a new guided bomb would separate cleanly from the F-117. It was a pretty simple test, and all went smoothly. The bomb cleared the aircraft cleanly and we all went home.

Lockheed never called me back again and I went on to become the Administrative Pastor for a local church and teach an Aviation Seminar at a high school located at Flabob airport in Riverside, CA. It was a great career. I just had a blast, and I worked with the best people anyone could wish to work with.

Thank You, Lord. It was an e-ticket ride!

Key Points to Remember

- People tried to intimidate me but respected someone who stood firm.

- My job was, "Not to do it but to get it done."

- I had confidence to make decisions because Bob never cut the rug out from under me.

- I went from door-to-door to find places for our people to work.

- "Argue with the boss until he says, 'No.' three times, then shut up!"

- Playing with things like Ford coils helped lead me to a career in electrical engineering.

- I decided I would take control and make the necessary decisions.

- You can not walk off work in the middle of a shift!

- All balances are six-component balances.

- Lift is always perpendicular to the wind, and drag is always in the wind direction, no matter what the angle of attack.

- Perhaps the most delicate measurement when calibrating a balance is proper leveling of the balance.

- Everything must be kept level throughout the calibration procedure.

- They say necessity is the mother of invention. I say laziness is the father.

- I said, "I don't know but we can try."

- It is a good idea to let management know what is going on before something happens and the s*#$ hits the fan.

- The Law of Spares: "Nothing will ever go bad, if you have a spare for it."

- A clean system is a good system.

- You NEVER replace a piece of working equipment with questionable equipment during a running wind tunnel test!

- Good men can passionately disagree over techniques.

- Straight forward troubleshooting and a steady application of basic principles will solve a big problem step-by-step.

- The weapons our military has should give the bad guys second thoughts before they start messin' with the good, 'ol U.S.A.!

- That's what testing is all about. Things don't always work the way you expect them to.

- It was almost as dangerous to stand behind that gun as in front of it.

- This scaling factor is called the Reynold's number.

- "Saving money by being efficient does the company no good if you lose a contract by not having the data you need in time."

- "It must be right. A Ph.D. developed it." That certainly did not reassure me.

- That is why an engineer must never accept an order to "just do it this way." Always ask, "What do you want to measure and why."

- "When you are in command, command."

- All strain gage balances react to six components of force or moment.

- You must be careful to know what you are doing!

- The stagnation point is the place where the airflow divides and part enters the inlet and the rest of the air goes outside along the missile.

- Some things never change.

- When you let the smoke out of an electrical system, it doesn't work anymore.

- A delay is better than a disaster.

Photo Reference List

Figure 1: Northrop 7x10 Low Speed Wind Tunnel, image taken by William Anderson, used by courtesy of his personal collection.

Figure 2: Bob and Roy, image taken by William Anderson, used by courtesy of his personal collection.

Figure 3: Northrop 2x2 Supersonic Wind Tunnel, image taken by William Anderson, used by courtesy of his personal collection.

Figure 4: NASA Able Corporation Series D Six Component Internal Strain Gage Balance. (1960). NASA. Retrieved May 2, 2022, from https://www.nasa.gov/sites/default/files/atoms/files/able_corporation_series_d_six_component_internal_strain_gage_balance.pdf

Figure 5: Vdjole. (2014, May 7). Wind Tunnel Balance. Wikimedia Commons. Retrieved January 2, 2022, from https://commons.wikimedia.org/wiki/File:Wind_tunnel_balance_-_monoblok.png

Figure 6: NASA. (n.d.). Internal Force Balance. NASA. Retrieved January 2, 2022, from https://www.grc.nasa.gov/www/k-12/airplane/tunbalint.html

Figure 7: NASA. (2021, May 13). Force Balance Coordinates. Force Balance Coordinates: Glenn Research Center. Retrieved January 2, 2022, from https://www.grc.nasa.gov/www/k-12/airplane/tunbalaxes.html

Figure 8: F5E models on calibration stands, image taken by William Anderson, used by courtesy of his personal collection.

Figure 9: Drag calibration by technicians, image taken by William Anderson, used by courtesy of his personal collection.

Figure 10: Sketch of Bubble Package showing orientation of electrolytic bubbles; sketch by William Anderson, used by courtesy of his personal collection.

Figure 11: NASA. (n.d.). Appendix F. NASA. Retrieved January 2, 2022, from https://history.nasa.gov/SP-4103/app-f.htm

Figure 12: Wikipedia contributors. (2021, June 30). Northrop X-21. Wikipedia. Retrieved January 2, 2022, from https://en.wikipedia.org/wiki/Northrop_X-21#/media/File:Northrop_X-21A_takeoff.jpg

Figure 13: Wikimedia.org. (2020, November 12). Hot Wire Anemometer. Wikimedia Commons File: Anémomètre à fil chaud, hot-wire anemometer. png. Retrieved January 2, 2022, from https://commons.wikimedia.org/wiki/File:An%C3%A9mom%C3%A8tre_%C3%A0_fil_chaud,_hot-wire_ anemometer.png

Figure 14: Lavi, R., Hall, G. R., & Stark, W. W. (1966, June 16). NASA, Full Scale Ground Proximity Investigtion of a VTOL fighter aircraft. NASA. Retrieved May 2, 2022, from https://ntrs.nasa.gov/api/citations/19680018761/downloads/19680018761.pdf

Figure 15: Wikimedia Foundation. (2022, January 11). Northrop YA-9. Wikipedia. Retrieved January 11, 2022, from https://en.wikipedia.org/wiki/Northrop_YA-9#/media/File:Northrop_YA-9_prototype.jpg

Figure 16: NASA. (n.d.). CH4-3. NASA. Retrieved January 2, 2022, from https://history.nasa.gov/SP-440/ch4-3.htm

Figure 17: Control room for the Northrop supersonic and hypersonic wind tunnels, image taken by William Anderson, used by courtesy of his personal collection.

Figure 18: Northrop 2x2 foot wind tunnel showing test section window with model mounted in tunnel, image taken by William Anderson, used by courtesy of his personal collection.

Figure 19: YF-17 model mounted in the Northrop 2x2 foot transonic wind tunnel, image taken by William Anderson, used by courtesy of his personal collection.

Figure 20: Schlieren of T-38 model at Mach 2, image taken by William Anderson, used by courtesy of his personal collection.

Figure 21: Schlieren of a model at Mach 10, image taken by William Anderson, used by courtesy of his personal collection.

Figure 22: Spark shadowgraph of same model at Mach 10, image taken by William Anderson, used by courtesy of his personal collection.

Figure 23: Wikimedia Foundation. (2020, September 25). Pontiac M39 20mm Cannon EASM 4Feb2010. Wikipedia. Retrieved January 2, 2022, from https://commons.wikimedia.org/wiki/File:Pontiac_M39_20mm_cannon_EASM_4Feb2010_(14611191813).jpg

Figure 24: Irving, B. (2006, March 7). X-15 Delta1. Flickr. Retrieved January 2, 2022, from https://www.flickr.com/photos/flyingsinger/109291419

Figure 25: Pilot flying the simulator, image taken by William Anderson, used by courtesy of his personal collection.

Figure 26: Image 25: Flutter model in Northrop 7x10 wind tunnel, image taken by William Anderson, used by courtesy of his personal collection.

Figure 26: PICRYL. (2022, April 13). Computers reading from the Manometer Board of7the 16 Foot Wind Tunnel. Retrieved April 13, 2022, from https://picryl.com/media/computers-reading-from-the-manometer-board-of-the-16-foot-wind-tunnel-b5a8a7

Figure 28: Used with permission from Scanivalve permission by Addison Pemberton, President, Scannivalve Corp. Scanivalve. (2020, March 2). ZOC33 miniature pressure scanner. Retrieved January 2, 2022, from https://scanivalve.com/products/pressure-measurement/miniature-analog-pressure-scanners/zoc33-miniature-pressure-scanner/

Figure 29: A typical "compressor can" consisting of 8 rakes holding 5 Kulite transducers each, image taken by William Anderson, used by courtesy of his personal collection.

Figure 30: Arnold Air Force Base. (n.d.-b). Recognizing the 25th anniversary of Desert Storm: AEDC tested technology that gave U.S. military the edge. Retrieved May 2, 2022, from https://www.arnold.af.mil/News/Photos/igphoto/2001500921/

Figure 31: Arnold Air Force Base. (n.d.-c). The big picture. Retrieved January 2, 2022, from https://www.arnold.af.mil/News/Photos/igphoto/2000690772/

Figure 32: Arnold Air Force Base Moving Wind Tunnel photos. (n.d.). Arnold Engineer Development Complex Photos. Retrieved March 3, 2022, from https://www.arnold.af.mil/News/Photos/?igsearch=moving%20wind%20tunnel

Figure 33: Arnold Air Force Base Moving Wind Tunnel photos. (n.d.). Arnold Engineer Development Complex Photos. Retrieved March 3, 2022, from https://www.arnold.af.mil/News/Photos/?igsearch=moving%20wind%20tunnel

Figure 34: Arnold Air Force Base Moving Wind Tunnel photos. (n.d.). Arnold Engineer Development Complex Photos. Retrieved March 3, 2022, from https://www.arnold.af.mil/News/Photos/?igsearch=moving%20wind%20tunnel

Figure 35: GE Analog Distortion Analyzer, image taken by William Anderson, used by courtesy of his personal collection.

Figure 36: Arnold Air Force Base. (n.d.-c). Recognizing the 25th anniversary of Desert Storm: AEDC tested technology that gave U.S. military the edge. Retrieved May 2, 2022, from https://www.arnold.af.mil/News/Photos/igphoto/2001500920/

Figure 37: USAF. (2017, September 5). USAF Northrop F20-1 300.jpg. Wikimedia Commons: Northrop F-20 Tigershark. Retrieved January 2, 2022, from https://commons.wikimedia.org/wiki/File:USAF_Northrop_F20-

1_300.jpg

Figure 38: Arnold Air Force Base. (n.d.-b). Significant investment allows for replacement of PWT Main Drive power equipment. Retrieved January 2, 2022, from https://www.arnold.af.mil/News/Photos/igphoto/2002049266/

Figure 39: USAF. (2007, October 30). Northrop - McDonnell Douglas YF-23. Flickr. Retrieved January 2, 2022, from https://www.flickr.com/photos/tom-margie/1804843479/in/photostream/

Figure 40: Wikipedia contributors. (2022, March 31). Drag curve. Wikipedia. Retrieved January 2, 2022, from https://en.wikipedia.org/wiki/Drag_curve#/media/File:DargPolarAL.png

Figure 41: Arnold Air Force Base. (n.d.). Navy fighter tests conducted in AEDC's 16-foot transonic tunnel. Retrieved January 2, 2022, from https://www.arnold.af.mil/News/Photos/igphoto/2000495259/

Figure 42: NASA. (n.d.). Areas of Ames Ingenuity: Wind Tunnel Testing. Retrieved January 2, 2022, from https://www.nasa.gov/centers/ames/research/area-wind-tunnels.html

Figure 43: NASA. (2021a, May 13). Aerodynamic Force Model. Retrieved January 2, 2022, from https://www.grc.nasa.gov/www/k-12/airplane/tunmodel.html

Figure 44: Arnold Air Force Base. (n.d.-c). Photos. https://www.arnold.af.mil/News/Photos/igpage/15/?igsearch=model%20windtunnel

Figure 45: Fan blades (Chicken-house fan) used at exit of Northrop Minitunnel, image taken by William Anderson, used by courtesy of his personal collection.

Figure 46: Laser light sheet photos of F-106 model, image taken by William Anderson, used by courtesy of his personal collection.

Figure 47: The plastic rotary water table sitting on the rate table, image taken by William Anderson, used by courtesy of his personal collection.

Figure 48: 0 Volts Applied, image taken by William Anderson, used by courtesy of his personal collection.

Figure 49: 30,000 Volts applied, image taken by William Anderson, used by courtesy of his personal collection.

Figure 50: The Mach = 2 plastic wind tunnel with Tesla coil, image taken by William Anderson, used by courtesy of his personal collection.

Figure 51: Lightning bolts and plasma in plastic tunnel with Tesla coil, image taken by William Anderson, used by courtesy of his personal collection.

Figure 52: NASA. (n.d.-b). NASA- Delta II rocket. NASA Image Library. Retrieved May 2, 2022, from https://images-assets.nasa.gov/image/9304431/9304431~thumb.jpg

Figure 53: Wikipedia contributors. (2022b, May 19). Lockheed Martin F-35 Lightning II. Wikipedia. Retrieved January 2, 2022, from https://en.wikipedia.org/wiki/Lockheed_Martin_F-35_Lightning_II#/media/File:F-35A_flight_(cropped).jpg

Figure 54: USAF. (2008, October 24). F-35 at Edwards. Wikimedia Commons. Retrieved January 2, 2022, from https://commons.wikimedia.org/wiki/File:F-35_at_Edwards.jpg

Figure 55: PICRYL. (2022a, April 12). 5.75% Scale Boeing BWB-0009G Model in NASA Langley 14x22 Foot Tu. Retrieved January 2, 2022, from https://picryl.com/media/575-scale-boeing-bwb-0009g-model-in-nasa-langley-14x22-foot-tu-9fba5a

Manufactured by Amazon.ca
Bolton, ON

33646844R00099